JUNIOR PRAISE

Compiled by
Peter Horrobin and Greg Leavers

MUSIC EDITION

Marshall Pickering
An Imprint of HarperCollins*Publishers*

First published in Great Britain in 1986 by
Marshall Morgan & Scott Publications Ltd

Reprinted: 2000
Impression number: 15 14 13 12 11 10 09 08

Marshall Pickering is an imprint of
HarperCollins*Religious*
Part of HarperCollins*Publishers*
77–85 Fulham Palace Road,
Hammersmith, London W6 8JB

Compilation Copyright © 1986 by
Peter Horrobin & Greg Leavers

The Compilers assert the moral right to
be identified as the compilers of this work

Printed and bound in Great Britain by
Omnia Books Limited, Glasgow

A catalogue record for this book
is available from the British Library

ISBN 0-551-01293-5

Words edition: 0-551-01366-4 (single copy)
0-551-01292-7 (pack of 25)
0-551-01572-1 (easy-to-read)

Introduction

Junior Praise is a compilation of hymns, songs, choruses and spirituals suitable for children and young people. It draws on our rich heritage of traditional hymns and songs, as well as the many items of contemporary music and words now available.

Compiling any hymn book is like choosing a handful of stones off a pebble beach — the choice is bewildering. In making this selection we have sought to include material representative of the many different strands of Christian activity which are apparent in today's church. We have also ensured that there is a wide range of seasonal items for the major Christian festivals such as Christmas, Easter and Pentecost.

Singing should be fun, so we have had this very much in mind when considering possible items for inclusion — both in terms of the words and the music. With regard to the words, many of the more traditional hymns contain ideas that are totally foreign to today's children and are often littered with words such as *thee, thou* and *thine* which were the natural Christian language of an earlier age. We have eliminated all such instances, either by sensitive alteration to the originals or by using suitable updated versions from other sources.

We would strongly encourage musical involvement by children as well as just singing the words. With this in mind we have provided an easy to read melody line especially for recorders, flutes, xylophones, violins etc. There are also guitar chords, and to help young guitarists with difficult keys capo chords are added. The guitar chord symbols can of course be used equally well with many of the electronic keyboards which have an automatic chord facility. A chord chart will be found at the back of the book.

The sequence of the book is largely alphabetical — the exceptions being introduced by the publishers as a necessary economy in laying out the pages of the music edition. There are two indexes. One is alphabetical, the other being a subject guide to the contents.

Our over-riding purpose in offering this book for use in day schools and Sunday schools is that children should be encouraged through music to understand that God wants them to *enjoy* the experience of knowing, loving, serving and worshipping Him. The discipline which such Christian commitment makes possible will enable children to grow up as men and women of integrity in a world full of increasingly difficult moral dilemmas and temptations. We pray that all those who use this book will do so with these specific needs of children and young people at heart.

Peter Horrobin and Greg Leavers
March 1986

1 A boy gave to Jesus

Words and music Peter Horrobin
arr. Phil Burt

Capo 3

A boy gave to Jes-us five loaves and two fish, Not much you might say for a crowd; ___ But Je-sus, He took them, and smiled at the lad, Gave thanks to His Father and blessed them out loud.

1. A boy gave to Jesus five loaves and two fish,
   Not much you might say for a crowd;
   But Jesus, He took them, and smiled at the lad,
   Gave thanks to His father and blessed them out loud.

2. The boy then saw Jesus take loaves and the fish,
   Not much for the folk on that day;
   But Jesus, He broke them, and smiled at the lad,
   Gave bits to disciples to then give away.

3. Then all worshipped Jesus as enough loaves and fish
   Were given to every one there.
   But Jesus just watched them, and smiled at the lad
   Who'd given his lunch-box for Jesus to share.

1

2 Abba Father

Words and Music by
Dave Bilbrough

Abba, Father, let me be Yours and Yours a - lone. May my will for - ev - er be Ev - er - more Your own.

Abba, Father, let me be
Yours and Yours alone.
May my will for ever be
Evermore Your own.

Never let my heart grow cold,
Never let me go.
Abba, Father, let me be
Yours and Yours alone.

3 Alleluia, Alleluia, give thanks to the risen Lord

Words and music
Don Fishel
arr. Norman Warren

Capo 3

Al-le-lu-ia, al-le-lu-ia, give thanks to the ris-en Lord! Al-le-lu-ia, al-le-lu-ia, give praise to his name. Je-sus is Lord of all the earth. He is the king of cre-a-tion. Al-le-

(All-) al - le - lu - ia, al - le - lu - ia, thanks to the ri - sen Lord.

Al - le - lu - ia, al - le - lu - ia, praise to His name.

Alleluia, alleluia, give thanks to the risen Lord!
Alleluia, alleluia, give praise to his name.

1. Jesus is Lord of all the earth.
   He is the king of creation.
      Alleluia, alleluia . . .

2. Spread the good news through all the earth,
   Jesus has died and has risen.
      Alleluia, alleluia . . .

3. We have been crucified with Christ—
   Now we shall live forever.
      Alleluia, alleluia . . .

4. God has proclaimed the just reward—
   Life for all men, alleluia!
      Alleluia, alleluia . . .

5. Come let us praise the living God,
   Joyfully sing to our Saviour!
      Alleluia, alleluia . . .

4 All people that on earth do dwell

Roger Jones
arr. Phil Burt

All people that on earth do dwell Sing to the Lord with cheerful voice: Serve Him with joy, His prais-es tell, Come now be-fore Him and re-joice! Know that the Lord is God in-deed, He formed us all with-out our aid;

We are the flock He loves to feed, The sheep who by His hand are
made. _____ - dore.

1. All people that on earth do dwell
   Sing to the Lord with cheerful voice:
   Serve Him with joy, His praises tell,
   Come now before Him and rejoice!
   Know that the Lord is God indeed,
   He formed us all without our aid;
   We are the flock He loves to feed,
   The sheep who by His hand are made.

2. O enter then His gates with praise,
   And in His courts His love proclaim;
   Give thanks and bless Him all your days:
   Let every toungue confess His name.
   The Lord our mighty God is good,
   His mercy is for ever sure;
   His truth at all times firmly stood,
   And shall from age to age endure.

3. All people that on earth do dwell
   Sing to the Lord with cheerful voice:
   Serve Him with joy, His praises tell,
   Come now before Him and rejoice!
   Praise God the Father, God the Son,
   And God the Spirit evermore;
   All praise to God the three-in-one,
   Let heaven rejoice and earth adore!

W. Kethe, d. 1594
© in this version *Jubilate Hymns*

5 All over the world

Roy Turner

1. All over the world the Spirit is moving,
   All over the world as the prophet said it would be;
   All over the world there's a mighty revelation
   Of the glory of the Lord, as the waters cover the sea.

2. All over His church God's Spirit is moving,
   All over His church as the prophet said it would be;
   All over His church there's a mighty revelation
   Of the glory of the Lord, as the waters cover the sea.

3. Right here in this place the Spirit is moving,
   Right here in this place as the prophet said it would be;
   Right here in this place there's a mighty revelation
   Of the glory of the Lord, as the waters cover the sea.

6 All things bright and beautiful (i)

English traditional melody
seventeenth century
arr. M. Shaw (1875-1958)

ROYAL OAK 7676 and chorus

All things bright and beau-ti-ful, All crea-tures great and small,

All things wise and won-der-ful, The Lord God made them all.

1. Each lit-tle flower that o-pens, Each lit-tle bird that sings, He_

made their glow-ing co-lours, He made their ti-ny wings.

Following verses are printed overleaf

All things bright and beautiful (ii)

7.6.7.6. and chorus

W.H. Monk (1823-1889)

All things bright and beautiful,
All creatures great and small,
All things wise and wonderful,
The Lord God made them all.

1. Each little flower that opens,
   Each little bird that sings,
   He made their glowing colours,
   He made their tiny wings.
   All things bright . . .

2. The purple headed mountain,
   The river running by,
   The sunset, and the morning
   That brightens up the sky;
   All things bright . . .

3. The cold wind in the winter,
   The pleasant summer sun,
   The ripe fruits in the garden,
   He made them every one.
   All things bright . . .

4. He gave us eyes to see them,
   And lips that we might tell
   How great is God almighty,
   Who has made all things well.
   All things bright . . .

Cecil F. Alexander, 1818-1895

7 All around me, Lord

Words and music
Greg Leavers
arr. Phil Burt

A round in 3 parts

All around me, Lord, I see Your goodness,
All creation sings Your praises,
All the world cries, 'God is love!'

8 Amazing grace

Traditional
arr. Roland Fudge

AMAZING GRACE C.M.

A - ma - zing grace! How sweet the sound That saved a__ wretch like me._____ I once____ was__ lost, but now____ am__ found, Was blind, but__ now I see._____

1. Amazing grace! How sweet the sound
That saved a wretch like me.
I once was lost, but now am found,
Was blind, but now I see.

2. 'Twas grace that taught my heart to fear,
And grace my fears relieved.
How precious did that grace appear
The hour I first believed.

3. Through many dangers, toils and snares,
I have already come;
'Tis grace has brought me safe thus far,
And grace will lead me home.

4. When we've been there ten thousand years,
Bright shining as the sun,
We've no less days to sing God's praise
Than when we've first begun.

John Newton, 1725-1807

9 As with gladness

DIX 77.77.77

Adapted from a chorale by C. Kocher (1786-1872)

As with glad-ness men of old   Did the guid-ing   star be-hold;
As with joy they hailed its light,   Lead-ing on-ward, beam-ing bright,

So, most gra-cious God,   may we   Led by You for   ev - er   be.

1. As with gladness men of old
   Did the guiding star behold;
   As with joy they hailed its light,
   Leading onward, beaming bright,
   So, most gracious God, may we
   Led by You forever be.

2. As with joyful steps they sped,
   Saviour, to Your lowly bed,
   There to bend the knee before
   You whom heaven and earth adore,
   So may we with one accord,
   Seek forgiveness from our Lord.

3. As they offered gifts most rare
   Gold and frankincense and myrrh
   So may we cleansed from our sin
   Lives of service now begin
   As in love our treasures bring,
   Christ, to You our heavenly King.

4. Holy Jesus, every day
   Keep us in the narrow way;
   And, when earthly things are past,
   Bring our ransomed souls at last
   Where they need no star to guide,
   Where no clouds Your glory hide.

5. In the heavenly country bright
   Need they no created light
   You its light, its joy its crown,
   You its sun which goes not down.
   There for ever may we sing
   Hallelujahs to our King.

W.C. Dix, 1837-1898
Altered © 1986 Horrobin/Leavers

10 Angels from the realms of glory

IRIS 8.7.8.7 with chorus

French Carol Melody

An-gels from the realms of glo-ry, Wing your flight through all the earth;

Her-alds of cre - a - tion's sto-ry, Now pro-claim Mes - si - ah's birth!

Come ___ and

wor - ship, Christ, the new - born King. ___

wor - ship Christ, the new - born King.

1. Angels from the realms of glory,
   Wing your flight through all the earth;
   Heralds of creation's story,
   Now proclaim Messiah's birth!
   Come and worship,
   Christ, the new born King:
   Come and worship,
   Worship Christ the new-born King.

2. Shepherds in the fields abiding,
   Watching by your flocks at night,
   God with man is now residing:
   See, there shines the infant light!
   Come and worship . . .

3. Wise men, leave your contemplations!
   Brighter visions shine afar;
   Seek in him the hope of nations,
   You have seen his rising star:
   Come and worship . . .

4. Though an infant now we view him,
   He will share his Father's throne,
   Gather all the nations to him;
   Every knee shall then bow down:
   Come and worship . . .

J. Montgomery, 1771-1854
© in this version *Jubilate Hymns*

11 Ask! ask! ask!

arr. Phil Burt

Capo 3

Ask! Ask! Ask! and it shall be giv-en you; Seek! Seek! Seek! and you shall find; Knock! Knock! Knock! it shall be opened un-to you, Your Heavenly Fa-ther is so kind. He knows what is best for His chil-dren, In bo-dy, soul, and mind; So ask! Ask! Ask!

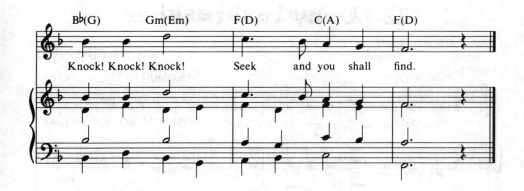

Knock! Knock! Knock! Seek and you shall find.

Ask! Ask! Ask! and it shall be given you;
Seek! Seek! Seek! and you shall find;
Knock! Knock! Knock! it shall be opened unto you,
Your Heavenly Father is so kind.
He knows what is best for His children,
In body, soul, and mind;
So ask! Ask! Ask! Knock! Knock! Knock!
Seek and you shall find.

Copyright control

12 Away in a manger

CRADLE SONG 11 11 11 11

W. J. Kirkpatrick (1838–1921)

1. Away in a manger, no crib for a bed,
   The little Lord Jesus laid down His sweet head.
   The stars in the bright sky looked down where He lay,
   The little Lord Jesus asleep in the hay.

2. The cattle are lowing, the Baby awakes,
   But little Lord Jesus, no crying He makes.
   I love You Lord Jesus! Look down from the sky,
   And stay by my side until morning is nigh.

3. Be near me, Lord Jesus; I ask You to stay
   Close by me for ever and love me, I pray.
   Bless all the dear children in Your tender care,
   And fit us for heaven to live with You there.

Attributed to Martin Luther, 1483-1546
American translation 1884

13 At the name of Jesus (i)

EVELYNS 6 5 6 5 D

W.H. Monk (1823-1889)

At the name of Je - sus Ev - ery knee shall bow,

Ev - ery tongue con - fess__ Him King of glo - ry now. __

'Tis the Fa - ther's plea - sure We should call Him Lord,

Who from the beg - in - ning Was the migh - ty Word:

At the name of Jesus (ii)

CAMBERWELL 6 5 6 5 D

Michael Brierley (b.1932)

At the name of Je-sus
Ev-ery knee shall bow,
Ev-ery tongue con-fess Him
King of glo-ry now.
'Tis the Fa-ther's plea-sure
We should call Him Lord,
Who from the be-gin-ning Was the migh-ty Word:

vv. 1-5

1. At the name of Jesus
   Every knee shall bow,
   Every tongue confess Him
   King of glory now.
   'Tis the Father's pleasure
   We should call Him Lord,
   Who from the beginning
   Was the mighty Word:

2. Humbled for a season,
   To receive a name
   From the lips of sinners
   Unto whom He came,
   Faithfully He lived here
   Spotless to the last,
   Raised was He victorious,
   When from death He passed;

3. Lifted high triumphant
   Far above the world,
   Into heaven's glory
   Our ascended Lord;
   To the throne of Godhead,
   At the Father's side,
   There He reigns resplendent
   Who for man had died.

4. In your hearts enthrone Him;
   There let Him subdue
   All that is not holy,
   All that is not true:
   Crown Him as your captain
   In temptation's hour,
   Let His will enfold you
   In its light and power.

5. Brothers, this Lord Jesus
   Shall return again,
   With His Father's glory,
   With His angel-train;
   For all wreaths of empire
   Meet upon His brow,
   And our hearts confess Him
   King of glory now.

Caroline Noel, 1817-1877
Altered © 1986 Horrobin/Leavers

14 Be bold

Words and music
Morris Chapman
arr. Andy Silver

Be bold ___ Be strong ___ for the Lord your God is with you, Be bold ___ Be strong for the Lord your God is with you, I am not a - fraid (No! No! No!) I am not dis-

Be bold, Be strong, for the Lord your God is with you,
Be bold, Be strong, for the Lord your God is with you,
I am not afraid (No! No! No!)
I am not dismayed,
For I'm walking in faith and victory,
Come on and walk in faith and victory
For the Lord your God is with you.

15 Behold, what manner of love

I JOHN 3:1
2-Part Round

Words and music
Patricia Van Tine

Be - hold, what man - ner of love the Fa - ther has giv - en un - to us,____ Be - hold, what man - ner of love the Fa-ther has giv - en un - to us, That we ____ should be called the sons ___ of God,

That we should be called the sons of God.

Behold, what manner of love the Father has given unto us,
Behold, what manner of love the Father has given unto us,
That we should be called the sons of God,
That we should be called the sons of God.

16 Big man

Words and music
Graham Kendrick
arr. Phil Burt

Big man stan-ding by the blue wa-ter-side, Men-ding nets by the blue sea. A - long came Je-sus, He said, 'Si-mon Pe-ter, won't you leave your nets and come fol - low me.' 'You don't need an - y-thing, I've got ev - 'ry-thing But Pe - ter, its gon - na be a

26

1. Big man standing by the blue waterside,
   Mending nets by the blue sea.
   Along came Jesus, He said,
   'Simon Peter, won't you leave your nets and come follow me.'

   You don't need anything, I've got everything
   But Peter, its gonna be a hard way.
   You don't have to worry now, come on and hurry now,
   I'll walk beside you every day.

2. Life wasn't easy for the big fisherman,
   But still he followed till his dying day.
   Along came Jesus, He said,
   'Simon Peter, There's a place in heaven where you can stay.'
      You don't need anything, . . .

17 Bind us together Lord

B. Gillman
arr. Norman Warren

Bind us togeth-er Lord, bind us togeth-er with cords that cannot be bro - ken;

Bind us to-geth-er Lord, bind us to-geth-er, O bind us to-geth-er with love!

There is on-ly one God, There is on-ly one King,

There is on-ly one Bo-dy___ That is why__ we sing:___

Words and music © 1977 Kingsway's Thankyou Music,
P O Box 75, Eastbourne, East Sussex BN23 6NW

Bind us together Lord,
Bind us together with cords
  that cannot be broken,
Bind us together Lord,
Bind us together, O bind us
  together with love.

2. Made for the glory of God,
   Purchased by His precious Son.
   Born with the right to be clean,
   For Jesus the victory has won.
     Bind us together. . .

1. There is only one God,
   There is only one King,
   There is only one Body
   That is why we sing:
     Bind us together. . .

3. You are the family of God.
   You are the promise divine.
   You are God's chosen desire.
   You are the glorious new wine.
     Bind us together. . .

18 Barabbas was a bad man

Words and music
Peter Horrobin

1. Barabbas was a bad man,
   Condemned to die was he,
   He'd done so many awful things,
   Was bad as bad could be.

2. But, Jesus was a good man
   God's only son was He.
   He did so many lovely things,
   The blind He made to see.

3. But Jesus some folk hated,
   They called "Put Him away".
   When Pilate made them choose the one
   To free that fatal day.

4. So Jesus though a good man
   Was killed on Calvary,
   But three days on He rose again
   To live eternally.

19 Bless the Lord, O my soul

Composer unknown
arr. R. Fudge

With breadth

Bless the Lord, O my soul,
Bless the Lord, O my soul,
And all that is within me } *Repeat*
Bless His holy name,

King of Kings (For ever and ever)
Lord of Lords (For ever and ever)
King of Kings (For ever and ever)
King of Kings and Lord of Lords.

Bless the Lord, O my soul,
Bless the Lord, O my soul,
And all that is within me } *Repeat*
Bless His holy name.

Copyright control

20 Blessed assurance

Irregular

Mrs. J.F. Knapp (1839-1908)

Bless-ed ass - ur - ance, Je-sus is mine:___ O what a
fore-taste of glo-ry di - vine!___ Heir of sal - va-tion, pur-chase of
God;___ Born of His Spi - rit, washed in His blood.___
This is my sto - ry, this is my song,___ Prais-ing my

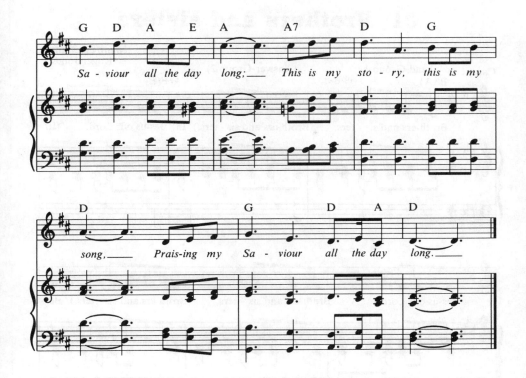

Sa - viour all the day long;___ This is my sto - ry, this is my song,___ Prais-ing my Sa - viour all the day long.___

1. Blessed assurance, Jesus is mine:
   O what a foretaste of glory divine!
   Heir of salvation, purchase of God;
   Born of His Spirit, washed in His blood.
   This is my story, this is my song,
   Praising my Saviour all the day long.

2. Perfect submission, perfect delight,
   Visions of rapture burst on my sight;
   Angels descending, bring from above
   Echoes of mercy, whispers of love.
   This is my story . . .

3. Perfect submission, all is at rest,
   I in my Saviour am happy and blest;
   Watching and waiting, looking above,
   Filled with His goodness, lost in His love.
   This is my story . . .

   Frances Van Alstyne, 1820-1915

33

21 Brothers and sisters

Words and music
Roger Jones

Broth-ers and sis - ters, (Broth-ers and sis - ters,) In Jes-us our Lord, (In Jes-us our Lord,) Broth-ers and sis - ters, (Broth-ers and sis - ters,) Be -liev-ing his word! (Be-liev-ing his word!) Now we're un-i - ted, (Now we're un-i - ted,) Made one in his love, (Made one in his love, We're

1. Brothers and sisters,
   In Jesus our Lord.
   Brothers and sisters,
   Believing His word!
   Now we're united,
   Made one in His love.
   We're brothers and sisters,
   In Jesus our Lord!

2. Jesus has saved us,
   From sin set us free.
   Always His people
   Together we'll be!
   This is the story
   We're telling the world!
   We're brothers and sisters,
   In Jesus our Lord!

3. Jesus has told us
   To be of good cheer,
   For He is with us,
   His Spirit is here!
   He gives us power,
   His message to share.
   We're brothers and sisters,
   In Jesus our Lord.

22 Be still and know

Arrangement
Roland Fudge

1. Be still and know that I am God;
   Be still and know that I am God;
   Be still and know that I am God.

2. I am the Lord that healeth thee,
   I am the Lord that healeth thee,
   I am the Lord that healeth thee.

3. In You, O Lord, I put my trust,
   In You, O Lord, I put my trust,
   In You, O Lord, I put my trust.

Copyright control

23 By blue Galilee

Words and music
E. H. Swinstead (d. 1976)

By blue Ga-li-lee Je-sus walked of old, By blue Ga-li-lee won-drous things He told. Sav-iour still my teach-er be, show-ing won-drous things to me, As of old by Ga-li-lee, blue Ga-li - lee.

By blue Galilee Jesus walked of old,
By blue Galilee wondrous things He told.
Saviour, still my Teacher be,
Showing wondrous things to me,
As of old by Galilee, blue Galilee.

24 Children of Jerusalem

INFANT PRAISE 77.77 with chorus

From CURWEN'S *Tune Book*, 1842

Children of Jerusalem Sang the praise of Jesus' name: Children, too, of modern days, Join to sing the Saviour's praise.

Hark, hark, hark! While children's voices sing, Hark, hark,

hark! While chil-dren's voi-ces sing, Loud ho - san-nas,

loud ho-san-nas, loud ho - san - nas_ to our King.

1. Children of Jerusalem
   Sang the praise of Jesus' name:
   Children, too, of modern days,
   Join to sing the Saviour's praise.

   Hark! Hark! Hark! While children's voices sing
   Hark! Hark! Hark! While children's voices sing
   Loud hosannas, loud hosannas,
   Loud hosannas to our King.

2. We are taught to love the Lord,
   We are taught to read His word,
   We are taught the way to heaven:
   Praise for all to God be given.
       Hark! Hark! Hark! ...

3. Parents, teachers, old and young,
   All unite to swell the song;
   Higher let God's praises rise
   As hosannas fill the skies.
       Hark! Hark! Hark! ...

   John Henley, 1800-1842
   Altered © 1986 Horrobin/Leavers

25 Christ triumphant

M. Saward

M.A. Baughen

With triumphant vigour

Capo 3

crown _____ The high re - nown

The e - ter - nal name. _____

1. Christ triumphant ever reigning,
    Saviour, Master, King,
    Lord of heav'n, our lives sustaining,
    Hear us as we sing:

    Yours the glory and the crown,
    The high renown,
    The eternal name.

2. Word incarnate, truth revealing,
    Son of Man on earth!
    Power and majesty concealing
    By your humble birth:
        Yours the glory . . .

3. Suffering servant, scorned, ill-treated,
    Victim crucified!
    Death is through the cross defeated,
    Sinners justified:
        Yours the glory . . .

4. Priestly King, enthroned for ever
    High in heaven above!
    Sin and death and hell shall never
    Stifle hymns of love:
        Yours the glory . . .

5. So, our hearts and voices raising
    Through the ages long,
    Ceaselessly upon You gazing,
    This shall be our song:
        Yours the glory . . .

© *Michael Saward / Jubilate Hymns*

26 Clap your hands all you people

Based on Psalm 47:1

Jimmy Owens
arr. David Peacock

This may be sung as a round

Clap your hands all you people,
Shout unto God with a voice of triumph.
Clap your hands all you people,
Shout unto God with a voice of praise!

Hosanna, Hosanna,
Shout unto God with a voice of triumph.
Praise Him, Praise Him,
Shout unto God with a voice of praise!

27 Cleanse me from my sin

Words and music
R. Hudson Pope (1879–1967)

Cleanse me from my sin, Lord, put Your pow'r within, Lord,
Take me as I am, Lord, and make me all Your own.
Keep me day by day, Lord, in Your perfect way, Lord,
Make my heart Your palace, and Your royal throne.

28 Colours of day
(Light up the fire)

Words and music: Sue McClellan,
John Pac, Keith Ryecroft
arr Douglas Coombes

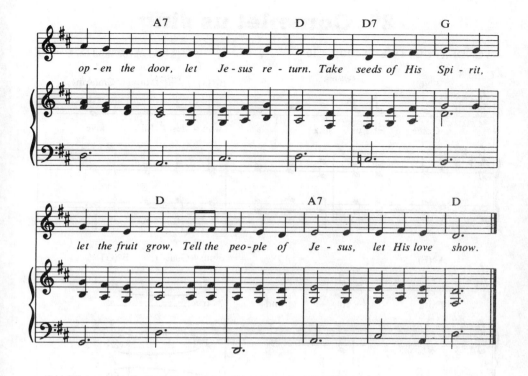

op - en the door, let Je - sus re - turn. Take seeds of His Spi - rit,
let the fruit grow, Tell the peo-ple of Je - sus, let His love show.

1. Colours of day dawn into the mind,
   The sun has come up, the night is behind.
   Go down in the city, into the street,
   And let's give the message to the people we meet.

   So light up the fire and let the flame burn,
   Open the door, let Jesus return.
   Take seeds of His Spirit, let the fruit grow,
   Tell the people of Jesus, let His love show.

2. Go through the park, on into the town;
   The sun still shines on, it never goes down.
   The light of the world is risen again;
   The people of darkness are needing our friend.
       So light up the fire . . .

3. Open your eyes, look into the sky,
   The darkness has come, the sun came to die.
   The evening draws on, the sun disappears,
   But Jesus is living, His Spirit is near.
       So light up the fire . . .

29 Come let us sing

WONDERFUL LOVE 10 4 10 7 4 10

F.L. Wiseman (1858-1944)

Come let us sing of a won-der-ful love,
Faith - ful and true;
Out of the heart of the Fa-ther a-bove,
Stream - ing to me and to you:

Music © Methodist Conference,
used by permission of the Methodist Publishing House

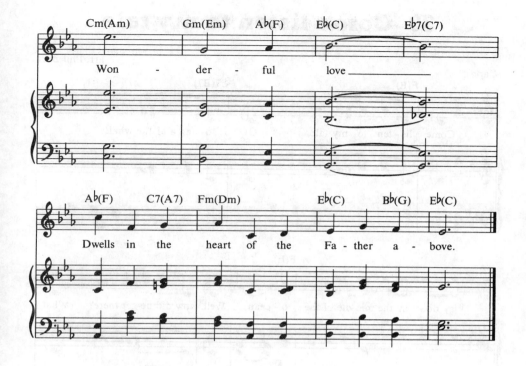

Won - der - ful love ____

Dwells in the heart of the Fa - ther a - bove.

1. Come let us sing of a wonderful love,
   Faithful and true;
   Out of the heart of the Father above,
   Streaming to me and to you:
   Wonderful love
   Dwells in the heart of the Father above.

2. Jesus, the Saviour, this gospel to tell,
   Joyfully came,
   Came with the helpless and hopeless to dwell,
   Sharing their sorrow and shame;
   Seeking the lost,
   Saving, redeeming at measureless cost.

3. Jesus is seeking all lost people yet;
   Why can't they see?
   Turning to Him He forgives and forgets,
   Longing to set their hearts free.
   Wonderful love
   Dwells in the heart of the Father above.

4. Come fill my heart with Your wonderful love,
   Come and abide,
   Lifting my life till it rises above
   Envy and falsehood and pride;
   Seeking to live
   Life that is humble, with strength that You give.

Robert Walmsley, 1831-1905.
Altered © 1986 Horrobin/Leavers

30 Come listen to my tale

arr. Phil Burt

Come listen to my tale,
Of Jonah and the whale,
Way down in the middle of the ocean,
Well, how did he get there?
Whatever did he wear?
Way down in the middle of the ocean.
A preaching he should be
At Nineveh you see
To disobey's a very foolish notion.
But God forgave His sin,
Salvation entered in,
Way down in the middle of the
Way down in the middle of the
Way down in the middle of the ocean.

31 Come on let's get up and go

Words and music
Graham Kendrick
arr. Phil Burt

Come on, let's get up and go, Let ev-'ry-one know. We've got a

rea-son to shout and to sing 'Cause Je - sus

loves us And that's a won-der-ful thing. *Fine*

Go! go! go! go! get up and go, Don't be slee - py or

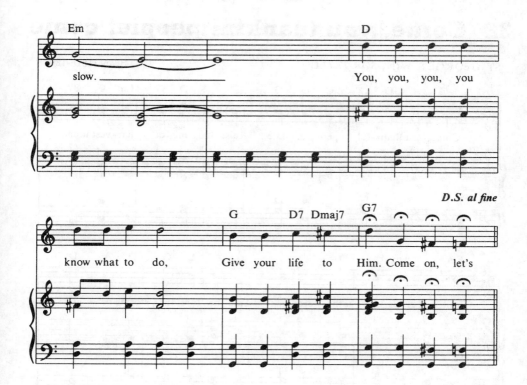

Come on, let's get up and go,
Let everyone know.
We've got a reason to shout and to sing
'Cause Jesus loves us
And that's a wonderful thing.

Go! go! go! go! get up and go,
Don't be sleepy or slow.
You, you, you, you know what to do,
Give your life to Him.

Come on, let's get up and go,
Let everyone know.
We've got a reason to shout and to sing
'Cause Jesus loves us
And that's a wonderful thing.

32 Come, you thankful people, come

ST. GEORGE'S, WINDSOR 77.77.D

G.J. Elvey (1816-1893)

Come, you thank-ful peo-ple, come, Raise the song of har-vest home!

Fruit and crops are gath - ered in Safe be-fore the storms be - gin:

God, our ma-ker will pro-vide For our needs to be sup - plied;

Come, with all His peo - ple, come, Raise the song of har-vest home!

1. Come, you thankful people, come,
   Raise the song of harvest home!
   Fruit and crops are gathered in
   Safe before the storms begin:
   God our maker will provide
   For our needs to be supplied;
   Come, with all His people, come,
   Raise the song of harvest home!

2. All the world is God's own field,
   Harvests for His praise to yield;
   Wheat and weeds together sown
   Here for joy or sorrow grown:
   First the blade and then the ear,
   Then the full corn shall appear—
   Lord of harvest, grant that we
   Wholesome grain and pure may be.

3. For the Lord our God shall come
   And shall bring His harvest home;
   He Himself on that great day,
   Worthless things shall take away,
   Give His angels charge at last
   In the fire the weeds to cast,
   But the fruitful ears to store
   In His care for evermore.

4. Even so, Lord, quickly come—
   Bring Your final harvest home!
   Gather all Your people in
   Free from sorrow, free from sin,
   There together purified,
   Ever thankful at Your side—
   Come, with all Your angels, come,
   Bring that glorious harvest home!

H. Alford, 1810-1871
© in this version *Jubilate Hymns*

33 Come to Jesus, He's amazing

Words by Peter Horrobin
Music by Phil Burt

Come to Jesus, "He's a-mazing" Peo - ple cried out when they saw,

People walking, who were crippled, Blind eyes see-ing, healed once more.

Come to Jesus, "He's amazing"
People cried out when they saw,
People walking, who were crippled,
Blind eyes seeing, healed once more.

© *1986 Peter Horrobin*

34 Come and praise the Lord our King

Traditional
arr. Douglas Coombes

Come and praise the Lord our King, Hallelujah,
Come and praise the Lord our King, Hallelujah.

1. Christ was born in Bethlehem, Hallelujah,
   Son of God and Son of Man, Hallelujah.
   Come and praise . . .

2. From Him love and wisdom came, Hallelujah;
   All His life was free from blame, Hallelujah.
   Come and praise . . .

3. Jesus died at Calvary, Hallelujah,
   Rose again triumphantly, Hallelujah.
   Come and praise . . .

4. He will cleanse us from our sin, Hallelujah,
   If we live by faith in Him, Hallelujah.
   Come and praise . . .

5. He will be with us today, Hallelujah,
   And forever with us stay, Hallelujah.
   Come and praise . . .

6. We will live with Him one day, Hallelujah,
   And for ever with Him stay, Hallelujah:
   Come and praise . . .

Copyright control

35 Deep and wide

Sidney E. Cox

arr. Andy Silver

Deep and wide, deep and wide,
There's a fountain flowing deep and wide;
Deep and wide, deep and wide,
There's a fountain flowing deep and wide.

36 Daniel was a man of prayer

arr. Phil Burt

Dan - iel was a man of prayer, Dai - ly
he prayed three times. Till one day they
had him cast In a den of li - ons.
In the den, in the den, Fear could

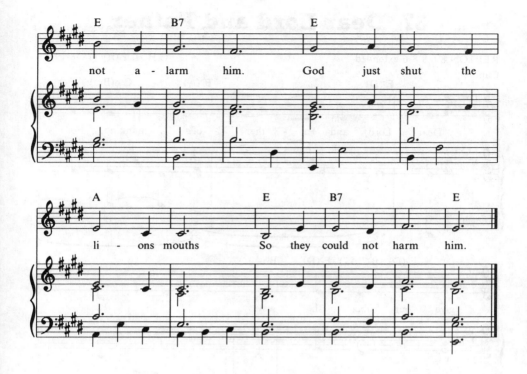

not a - larm him. God just shut the
li - ons mouths So they could not harm him.

Daniel was a man of prayer,
Daily he prayed three times.
Till one day they had him cast
In a den of lions.
In the den, in the den,
Fear could not alarm him.
God just shut the lions mouths
So they could not harm him.

Copyright control

37 Dear Lord and Father

REPTON 8 6 8 8 6 extended

C.H.H. Parry (1848-1918)

Capo 1

Dear Lord and Fa - ther of mankind, For -
give our fool - ish ways: Re -
clothe us in our right - ful mind; In pur - er lives Your
ser - vice ___ find, In ___ deep - er rev - erence

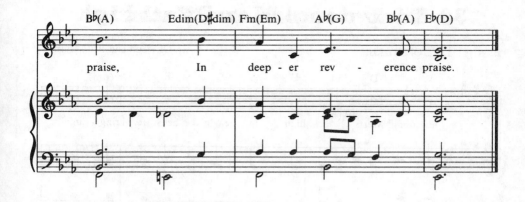

praise, In deep - er rev - erence praise.

1. Dear Lord and Father of mankind,
   Forgive our foolish ways:
   Reclothe us in our rightful mind;
   In purer lives Your service find,
       In deeper reverence praise,
       In deeper reverence praise.

2. In simple trust like theirs who heard,
   Beside the Syrian sea,
   The gracious calling of the Lord —
   Let us, like them, obey His word:
       'Rise up and follow me,
       Rise up and follow me!'

3. O sabbath rest by Galilee!
   O calm of hills above,
   When Jesus shared on bended knee
   The silence of eternity
       Interpreted by love,
       Interpreted by love!

4. With that deep hush subduing all
   Our words and works that drown
   The tender whisper of Your call,
   As noiseless let Your blessing fall
       As fell Your manna down,
       As fell Your manna down.

5. Drop Your still dews of quietness,
   Till all our strivings cease;
   Take from our souls the strain and stress,
   And let our ordered lives confess
       The beauty of Your peace,
       The beauty of Your peace.

6. Breathe through the heats of our desire
   Your coolness and Your balm;
   Let sense be dumb, let flesh retire,
   Speak through the earthquake, wind, and fire,
       O still small voice of calm,
       O still small voice of calm!

J.G. Whittier, 1807-1892
© in this version *Jubilate Hymns*

38 Ding dong! Merrily on high

BRANLE DE L'OFFICIAL

16th-century French melody
arr. C. Wood and B. V. Burnett

Ding dong! Merri - ly on high   In heav'n the bells are ring - ing:

Ding dong! Ve - ri - ly the sky   Is riv'n with an - gels sing - ing.

Glo - - - - - -

- - - - - ri - a, Ho -

- san - na in ex - cel - sis!

1. Ding dong! Merrily on high
   In heav'n the bells are ringing:
   Ding dong! Verily the sky
   Is riv'n with angels singing.
   Gloria, Hosanna in excelsis!
   Gloria, Hosanna in excelsis!

2. E'en so here below, below,
   Let steeple bells be swungen,
   And i-o, i-o, i-o,
   By priest and people sungen.
   Gloria, Hosanna in excelsis!
   Gloria, Hosanna in excelsis!

3. Pray you, dutifully prime
   Your matin chime, ye ringers;
   May you beautifully rime
   Your eve-time song, ye singers.
   Gloria, Hosanna in excelsis!
   Gloria, Hosanna in excelsis!

G. R. Woodward, 1859–1934
Copyright control

39 Don't build your house on the sandy land

Words and music by
Karen Lafferty

Don't build your house on the sand-y land,

Don't build it too near the shore. Well, it

might look kind of nice, But you'll have to build it twice, oh, you'll

have to build your house once more. Your bet-ter

* For round, when group 1 reaches this point, group 2 starts at the beginning.
Also, add Descant for a third group.

Don't build your house on the sandy land,
Don't build it too near the shore.
Well, it might look kind of nice,
But you'll have to build it twice,
Oh, you'll have to build your house once more.
You better build your house upon a rock,
Make a good foundation on a solid spot.
Oh, the storms may come and go,
But the peace of God you will know.

*Rock of ages cleft for me,
Let me hide myself in Thee.*

40 Do you want a Pilot?

Words and music
E. H. Swinstead (d. 1976)

Do you want a Pilot?
Signal then to Jesus;
Do you want a Pilot?
Bid Him come on board;
For He will safely guide,
Across the ocean wide,
Until you reach at last
The Heav'nly Harbour.

41 Father, hear the prayer we offer

MACHEN

Gott Wills

Fa-ther, hear the prayer we of - fer: Not for ease that prayer shall be,

But for strength that we may ev - er__ Live our lives cou - ra - geous-ly.

1. Father, hear the prayer we offer:
   Not for ease that prayer shall be,
   But for strength that we may ever
   Live our lives courageously.

2. Not for ever in green pastures
   Do we ask our way to be;
   But the steep and rugged pathway
   May we tread rejoicingly.

3. Not for ever by still waters
   Would we idly rest and stay;
   But would smite the living fountains
   From the rocks along our way.

4. Be our strength in hours of weakness,
   In our wanderings be our guide;
   Through endeavour, failure, danger,
   Father, always at our side.

   L. M. Willis, 1824–1908

42 Father, I place into Your hands

J. Hewer

Fa-ther, I place in - to Your hands The things that I can't do.

Fa-ther, I place in - to Your hands The times that I've been through.

Fa-ther, I place in - to Your hands The way that I should go, For I

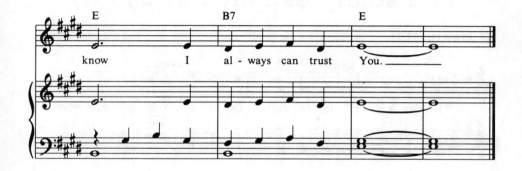

know I al - ways can trust You. _____

1. Father, I place into Your hands
   The things that I can't do.
   Father, I place into Your hands
   The times that I've been through.
   Father, I place into Your hands
   The way that I should go,
   For I know I always can trust You.

2. Father, I place into Your hands
   My friends and family.
   Father, I place into Your hands
   The things that trouble me.
   Father, I place into Your hands
   The person I would be,
   For I know I always can trust You.

3. Father, we love to seek Your face,
   We love to hear Your voice
   Father, we love to sing Your praise,
   And in your name rejoice.
   Father, we love to walk with You
   And in your presence rest,
   For we know we always can trust You.

4. Father, I want to be with You
   And do the things you do
   Father, I want to speak the words
   That You are speaking too.
   Father, I want to love the ones
   That You will draw to You,
   For I know that I am one with You.

43 Father, lead me day by day

ST. MARTIN 77.77.

Old French melody

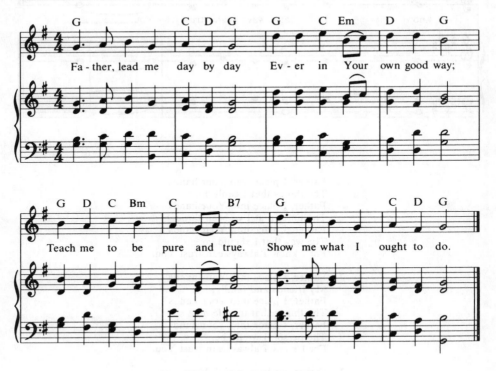

Fa-ther, lead me day by day Ev-er in Your own good way;

Teach me to be pure and true. Show me what I ought to do.

1. Father, lead me day by day
   Ever in Your own good way;
   Teach me to be pure and true.
   Show me what I ought to do.

2. When in danger, make me brave;
   Make me know that You can save.
   Keep me safe by Your dear side;
   Let me in Your love abide.

3. When I'm tempted to do wrong,
   Make me steadfast, wise and strong;
   And when all alone I stand,
   Shield me with Your mighty hand.

4. When my work seems hard and dry,
   May I never cease to try;
   Help me patiently to bear
   Pain and hardship, toil and care.

5. May I do the good I know,
   Be Your loving child below,
   Then at last in heaven share
   Life with You that's free from care.

J. P. Hopps, 1834–1912
Altered © 1986 Horrobin/Leavers

44 Father, we adore You

Terrye Coelho

Capo 1

Slowly, sustained

Fa - ther, we a - dore You, Lay our lives be - fore You: How we love You!

Can be sung as a 3-part round

1. Father, we adore You,
   Lay our lives before You:
   How we love You!

2. Jesus, we adore You,
   Lay our lives before You:
   How we love You!

3. Spirit, we adore You,
   Lay our lives before You:
   How we love You!

45 Father, we love You

GLORIFY YOUR NAME

Donna Adkins

Fa-ther we love You, We wor-ship and a-dore You, Glo-ri-fy Your name in all the earth. Glo-ri-fy Your name, Glo-ri-fy Your name, Glo-ri-fy Your

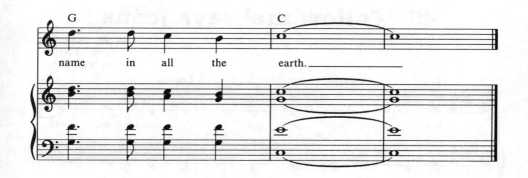

name in all the earth.

1. Father we love You,
   We worship and adore You,
   Glorify Your name in all the earth.
   Glorify Your name,
   Glorify Your name,
   Glorify Your name in all the earth.

2. Jesus, we love You,
   We worship and adore You,
   Glorify Your name in all the earth.
   Glorify Your name,
   Glorify Your name,
   Glorify Your name in all the earth.

3. Spirit, we love You,
   We worship and adore You,
   Glorify Your name in all the earth.
   Glorify Your name,
   Glorify Your name,
   Glorify Your name in all the earth.

46 'Follow me' says Jesus

Words and music
Greg Leavers
arr. Phil Burt

'Fol - low me' says Je - sus, 'I can keep you safe.

I am the Good Shep - herd, So

why not be my sheep.___ If you're lost and

lone - ly, I can keep you safe,___ I

gave my life to save you, So come, just fol-low me.'

'Follow me' says Jesus,
'I can keep you safe.
I am the Good Shepherd,
So why not be my sheep.
If you're lost and lonely
I can keep you safe,
I gave my life to save you,
So come, just follow me.'

47 For I'm building a people of power

D. Richards

Brightly

For I'm build-ing a peo-ple of pow-er___ And I'm mak-ing a peo-ple of praise, That will move thro' this land by My Spi-rit,___ And will glo-ri-fy my pre-cious Name. Build Your Church, Lord, Make us strong, Lord, Join our hearts, Lord, through Your Son, Make us

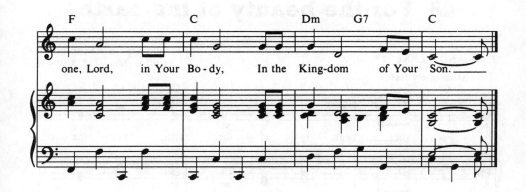

one, Lord,   in Your Bo-dy,   In the   King-dom   of Your Son.

For I'm building a people of power
And I'm making a people of praise,
That will move thro' this land by My Spirit,
And will glorify my precious Name.

Build Your Church, Lord,
Make us strong, Lord,
Join our hearts, Lord, through Your Son,
Make us one, Lord, in Your Body,
In the Kingdom of Your Son.

48 For the beauty of the earth

From an English melody
adpt. and harm.
Geoffrey Shaw (1879–1943)

ENGLAND'S LANE 77 77 77

Moderately fast

For the ____ beau - ty of the earth, For the
beau - ty ____ of the skies, For the ____ love which from our
birth O - ver and ____ a - round us lies, Fa - ther ____
un - to You we raise This our sa - cri - fice of praise.

1. For the beauty of the earth,
   For the beauty of the skies,
   For the love which from our birth
   Over and around us lies,
   Father unto You we raise
   This our sacrifice of praise.

2. For the beauty of each hour
   Of the day and of the night,
   Hill and vale and tree and flower,
   Sun and moon and stars of light,
   Father, unto You we raise
   This our sacrifice of praise.

3. For the joy of love from God,
   That we share on earth below.
   For our friends and family
   And the love that they can show,
   Father, unto You we raise
   This our sacrifice of praise.

4. For each perfect gift divine
   To our race so freely given,
   Thank You Lord that they are mine,
   Here on earth as gifts from heaven.
   Father, unto You we raise
   This our sacrifice of praise.

Folliott Pierpoint, 1835–1917
Altered © 1986 Horrobin/Leavers

49 From the rising of the sun

Psalm 113:3.1.2.

Paul Deming

From the rising of the sun
To the going down of the same
The Lord's name
Is to be praised.

Repeat

Praise ye the Lord,
Praise Him O ye servants of the Lord,
Praise the name of the Lord,
Blessed be the name of the Lord
From this time forth,
And for evermore.

50 Give me oil in my lamp

Anon
arr. Douglas Coombes

Sing ho-san-na, sing ho-san-na, Sing ho-san-na, to the King

1. Give me oil in my lamp, keep me burning.
   Give me oil in my lamp, I pray.
   Give me oil in my lamp, keep me burning,
   Keep me burning till the break of day.

   Sing hosanna, sing hosanna,
   Sing hosanna to the King of Kings!
   Sing hosanna, sing hosanna,
   Sing hosanna, to the King !

2. Give me joy in my heart, keep me singing.
   Give me joy in my heart, I pray.
   Give me joy in my heart, keep me singing,
   Keep me singing till the break of day.
       Sing hosanna . . .

3. Give me love in my heart, keep me serving.
   Give me love in my heart, I pray.
   Give me love in my heart, keep me serving,
   Keep me serving till the break of day.
       Sing hosanna . . .

4. Give me peace in my heart, keep me resting.
   Give me peace in my heart, I pray.
   Give me peace in my heart, keep me resting,
   Keep me resting till the break of day.
       Sing hosanna . . .

Anon
Copyright control

51 Glory to God in the highest

Words and music
Greg Leavers
arr. Phil Burt

Glo-ry to God in the high-est, Peace ___ ___ up-on earth. Je-sus Christ has come ___ to earth, That's why we sing, Je-sus the King, Je-sus has come for you. ___

Glory to God in the highest,
Peace upon the earth.
Jesus Christ has come to earth,
That's why we sing, Jesus the King,
Jesus has come for you.

1. The shepherds who were sitting there
   Were suddenly filled with fear,
   The dark night was filled with light
   Angels singing everywhere.
      Glory to God in . . .

2. The next time we hear a song
   Of worship from a heavenly throng,
   Will be when Jesus comes again,
   Then with triumph we'll all sing,
      Glory to God in . . .

© *Greg Leavers*

52 Glory to You my God, this night

TALLIS' CANON 8 8 8 8 (LM)

Shortened form of melody by
Thomas Tallis (1505-1585)

Glo-ry to You, my God, this night For all the bless-ings of the light;

Keep me, O keep me, King of kings, Be - neath your own al - migh-ty wings.

1. Glory to You, my God, this night
   For all the blessings of the light;
   Keep me, O keep me, King of kings,
   Beneath your own almighty wings.

2. Forgive me, Lord, through Your dear Son,
   The wrong that I this day have done,
   That peace with God and man may be,
   Before I sleep, restored to me.

3. Teach me to live, that I may dread
   The grave as little as my bed;
   Teach me to die, that so I may
   Rise glorious at the awesome day.

4. O may my soul on you repose
   And restful sleep my eyelids close;
   Sleep that shall me more vigorous make
   To serve my God when I awake.

5. If in the night I sleepless lie,
   My mind with peaceful thoughts supply;
   Let no dark dreams disturb my rest,
   No powers of evil me molest.

6. Praise God from whom all blessings flow
   In heaven above and earth below;
   One God, three persons, we adore
   To Him be praise for evermore!

T. Ken, 1637–1711

53 God is so good

Composer unknown
arr. David Peacock

God is so good, God is so good,

God is so good, he's so good to me.

1. God is so good,
   God is so good,
   God is so good,
   He's so good to me.

2. He took my sin,
   He took my sin,
   He took my sin,
   He's so good to me.

3. Now I am free,
   Now I am free,
   Now I am free,
   He's so good to me.

4. God is so good,
   He took my sin,
   Now I am free,
   He's so good to me.

Copyright control

54 God forgave my sin

Words and Music
Carol Owens

Smoothly

God for - gave my sin in Je - sus' name. I've been born a - gain in Je - sus' name. And in Je - sus' name I come to you To share his love as He told me

1. God forgave my sin in Jesus' name.
   I've been born again in Jesus' name.
   And in Jesus' name I come to you
   To share his love as He told me to.

   He said, 'Freely,
   Freely you have received;
   Freely, freely give.
   Go in my name and because you believe,
   Others will know that I live.'

2. All pow'r is giv'n in Jesus name.
   In earth and heav'n in Jesus' name.
   And in Jesus' name I come to you
   To share his pow'r as He told me to.
      He said, . . .

55 God is good

Ps 100:5; Heb 4:16

Graham Kendrick

God is good, we sing and shout it,
God is good, we celebrate.
God is good, no more we doubt it,
God is good, we know it's true.

And when I think of His love for me,
My heart fills with praise and I feel like dancing.
For in His heart there is room for me
And I run with arms opened wide.

56 God is our guide

FINLANDIA 11 10 11 10 11 10

J. Sibelius (1865-1957)
from *Finlandia*

God is our guide, our light and our de-live-rer,

He holds our hand, He walks be-side the way.

Lord, may our feet tread in the steps You taught us

To fol-low firm-ly as by faith each day,

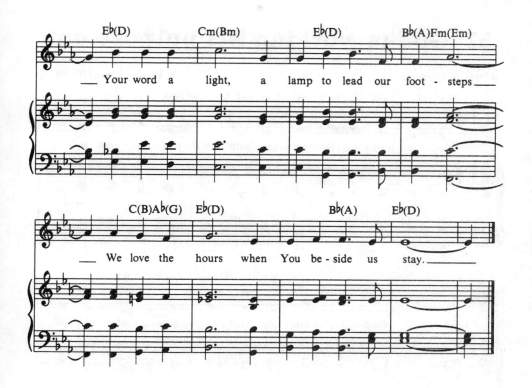

Your word a light, a lamp to lead our foot - steps

We love the hours when You be - side us stay.

1. God is our guide, our light and our deliverer,
   He holds our hand, He walks beside the way.
   Lord, may our feet tread in the steps You taught us
   To follow firmly as by faith each day,
   Your word a light, a lamp to lead our footsteps
   We love the hours when You beside us stay.

2. God is our peace, our help and our protector,
   We find His presence in the hour of need.
   Lord, though the storms of life may leave us trembling
   Your words of comfort bring us peace within.
   When we are weak and fear to face the future
   We find such comfort in Your loving arms.

3. God is our hope, our joy and our salvation,
   His love alone transforms the sinful heart.
   Lord how we sought Your Spirit's sweet renewing
   Your healing touch has filled our hearts with praise.
   We come and worship Jesus, Lord and Saviour,
   His love alone must fill our earthly days.

4. God is our strength, our rock and our redeemer
   In times of trouble and in times of joy.
   Lord, may our lives be full of sure thanksgiving
   Our lips be full of symphonies of praise.
   You gave us love, a risen, living Saviour,
   We bring ourselves a sacrifice of praise.

57 God is working His purpose out

BENSON Irregular

M.D. Kingham (1866-1927)

God is work-ing His pur-pose out, As year suc-ceeds to year: God is work-ing His pur-pose out, And the time is draw-ing near: Near-er and near-er draws the time, The time that shall sure-ly be, When the

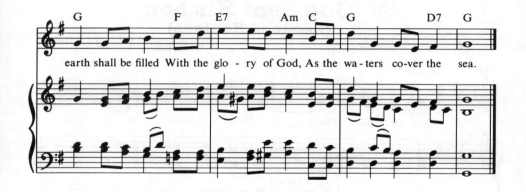

earth shall be filled With the glo - ry of God, As the wa - ters co-ver the sea.

1. God is working His purpose out,
   As year succeeds to year:
   God is working His purpose out,
   And the time is drawing near:
   Nearer and nearer draws the time,
   The time that shall surely be,
   When the earth shall be filled
   With the glory of God,
   As the waters cover the sea.

2. From utmost east to utmost west
   Wherever man has trod,
   By the mouth of many messengers
   Rings out the voice of God:
   Listen to me you continents,
   You islands look to me,
   That the earth may be filled
   With the glory of God,
   As the waters cover the sea.

3. We shall march in the strength of God,
   With the banner of Christ unfurled,
   That the light of the glorious gospel of truth
   May shine throughout the world;
   We shall fight with sorrow and sin
   To set their captives free,
   That the earth may be filled
   With the glory of God,
   As the waters cover the sea.

4. All we can do is nothing worth
   unless God blesses the deed;
   vainly we hope for the harvest tide
   Till God gives life to the seed:
   Nearer and nearer draws the time,
   The time that shall surely be,
   When the earth shall be filled
   With the glory of God,
   As the waters cover the sea.

A. Ainger, 1841-1919
© in this version *Jubilate Hymns*

58 God sent His Son
(Because He lives)

Gloria & William J. Gaither

William J. Gaither

God sent His Son, ____ they call Him Je-sus;

____ He came to love, ____ heal, and for- give;

____ He lived and died ____ to buy my par- don, ____

____ An emp-ty grave is there to prove my Saviour lives. ____

1. God sent His Son, they call Him Jesus;
He came to love, heal, and forgive;
He lived and died to buy my pardon,
An empty grave is there to prove my
        Saviour lives.

Because He lives I can face tomorrow;
Because He lives all fear is gone;
Because I know, I know He holds the future,
And life is worth the living just
                because He lives.

2. How sweet to hold a new-born baby,
And feel the pride, and joy he gives;
But greater still the calm assurance,
This child can face uncertain days
        because He lives.

    Because He lives . . .

3. And then one day I'll cross the river;
I'll fight life's final war with pain;
And then as death gives way to vict'ry,
I'll see the lights of glory and I'll
        know He lives.

    Because He lives . . .

59 God so loved the world

When group 1 gets to ***** group 2 starts at beginning

1. God so loved the world He sent to us Jesus,
   God so loved the world He sent His Son.
   Alleluia Jesus, Lord Jesus, Jesus;
   Alleluia Jesus, God sent His Son.

2. Jesus showed the world the love of the Father,
   Jesus showed the world how we must love.
   Alleluia Jesus, Lord Jesus, Jesus;
   Alleluia Jesus, God sent His Son.

60 God's not dead

arr. Phil Burt

God's not dead, (No)
He is alive.
God's not dead, (No)
He is alive.
God's not dead, (No) He is alive,

Serve Him with my hands,
Follow with my feet,
Love Him in my heart,
Know Him in my life;
For He's alive in me.

　　97

61 God whose farm is all creation

SHIPSTON

English Traditional Melody coll. Lucy Broadwood, arr. and harm. R. Vaughan Williams (1872-1958)

Capo 1

From the *English Hymnal* by permission of Oxford University Press.

1. God, whose farm is all creation,
   Take the gratitude we give;
   Take the finest of our harvest,
   Crops we grow that men may live.

2. Take our ploughing, seeding, reaping,
   Hopes and fears of sun and rain,
   All our thinking, planning, waiting,
   Ripened in this fruit and grain.

3. All our labour, all our watching,
   All our calendar of care,
   In these crops of Your creation,
   Take, O God; they are our prayer.

John Arlott, 1914–91 © Mrs B. M. Arlott

62 God whose Son
(When the Spirit came)

Words by Peter Horrobin

Music by Greg Leavers

God whose Son was once a man on earth Gave His life that men may live. Ris - en, our as - cen - ded Lord Ful - filled His pro - mised word. *When the Spi - rit came, the church was born, God's peo - ple shared in a bright new dawn. They*

1. God whose Son was once a man on earth
   Gave His life that men may live.
   Risen, our ascended Lord
   Fulfilled His promised word.

   When the Spirit came, the church was born,
   God's people shared in a bright new dawn.
   They healed the sick,
   They taught God's word,
   They sought the lost,
   They obeyed the Lord.
   And it's all because the Spirit came
   That the world will never be the same,
   Because the Spirit came.

2. God whose power fell on the early church,
   Sent to earth from heav'n above.
   Spirit led, by Him ordained
   They showed the world God's love.

   When the Spirit came, the church was born,
   God's people shared in a bright new dawn.
   They healed the sick,
   They taught God's word,
   They sought the lost,
   They obeyed the Lord.
   And it's all because the Spirit came
   That the world will never be the same,
   Because the Spirit came.

3. Pour Your Spirit on the church today,
   That Your life through me may flow.
   Spirit filled, I'll serve Your Name
   And live the truth I know.

   When the Spirit comes, new life is born,
   God's people share in a bright new dawn.
   We'll heal the sick,
   We'll teach God's word,
   We'll seek the lost,
   We'll obey the Lord.
   And it's all because the Spirit came
   That the world will never be the same,
   Because the Spirit came.

63 God who made the earth

SOMMERLIED 5 6 6 4

H. von Muller (1859–1938)

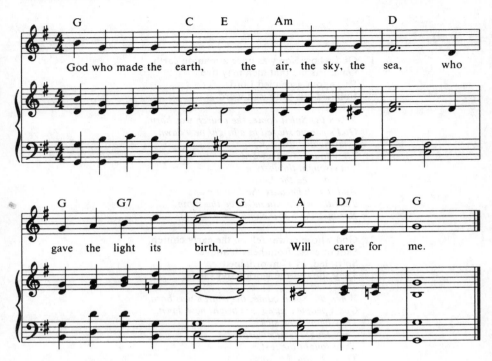

God who made the earth, the air, the sky, the sea, who gave the light its birth,___ Will care for me.

1. God who made the earth,
   The air, the sky, the sea,
   Who gave the light its birth,
   Will care for me.

2. God who made the grass,
   The flower, the fruit, the tree,
   The day and night to pass,
   Will care for me.

3. God who, made the sun,
   The moon, the stars, is He
   Who when life's clouds come on,
   Will care for me.

4. God who sent His Son
   To die on calvary,
   He, if I lean on Him,
   Will care for me.

5. God who gave me life,
   His servant here to be,
   Has promised in His word
   To care for me.

S. B. Rhodes, 1830–1904
Altered © 1986 Horrobin/Leavers

64 Great is Your faithfulness

11 10 11 10 and Chorus

W.M. Runyan (1870-1957)

Great is Your faith-ful-ness, O God my Fa-ther,

You have ful-filled all Your pro-mise to me;

You ne-ver fail and Your love is un-chang-ing

All You have been You for-e-ver will be.

Great is Your faith-ful-ness, Great is Your faith-ful-ness,

Morn - ing by morn - ing new mer - cies I see;

All I have need - ed Your hand has pro - vid - ed

Great is Your faith - ful-ness, Fa - ther, to me.

1. Great is Your faithfulness, O God my Father,
   You have fuilfilled all Your promise to me;
   You never fail and Your love is unchanging
   All You have been You for ever will be.

   Great is Your faithfulness,
   Great is Your faithfulness,
   Morning by morning new mercies I see;
   All I have needed Your hand has provided
   Great is Your faithfulness, Father, to me.

2. Summer and winter, and springtime and harvest,
   Sun, moon and stars in their courses above
   Join with all nature in eloquent witness
   To Your great faithfulness, mercy and love.
      Great is Your faithfulness . . .

3. Pardon for sin, and a peace everlasting,
   Your living presence to cheer and to guide;
   Strength for today, and bright hope for tomorrow,
   These are the blessings Your love will provide.
      Great is Your faithfulness . . .

T. O. Chisholm, 1866–1960
in this version Jubilate Hymns

65 Go, tell it on the mountain

Traditional melody
arr. Douglas Coombes

Go, tell it on the moun - tain, O - ver the hills and ev - 'ry-where;

Go, tell it on the moun - tain That Je - sus is His name.

He pos-sessed no ri - ches, no home to lay His head; He

saw the needs of oth - ers and cared for them in - stead.

Go, tell it on the mountain,
Over the hills and ev'rywhere;
Go, tell it on the mountain
That Jesus is His name.

1. He possessed no riches, no home to lay His head;
   He saw the needs of others and cared for them instead.
      Go, tell it . . .

2. He reached out and touched them, the blind, the deaf, the lame;
   He spoke and listened gladly to anyone who came.
      Go, tell it . . .

3. Some turned away in anger, with hatred in the eye;
   They tried Him and condemned Him, then led Him out to die.
      Go, tell it . . .

4. "Father, now forgive them" — those were the words He said;
   In three more days He was alive and risen from the dead.
      Go, tell it . . .

5. He still comes to people, His life moves through the lands;
   He uses us for speaking, He touches with our hands.
      Go, tell it . . .

66 Hallelujah, for the Lord our God

Dale Garratt

Triumphantly

Hal-le-lu-jah,_____ for the Lord our God the Al-migh-ty_____ reigns._____ Hal-le-lu-jah,_____ for the Lord our God the Al-migh-ty_____ reigns. Let us re-joice_____ and be

Hallelujah, for the Lord our God the Almighty reigns.
Hallelujah, for the Lord our God the Almighty reigns.
Let us rejoice and be glad
And give the Glory unto Him.
Hallelujah, for the Lord our God the Almighty reigns.

67 Hallelu, hallelu

Composer unknown
arr. E.J. Hume

Halle - lu, halle-lu, halle - lu, halle-lu-jah; We'll praise the Lord! Halle -
lu, hal-le-lu, hal-le - lu, hal-le-lu - jah; We'll praise the Lord!
We'll praise the Lord, hal-le-lu-jah! We'll praise the Lord, hal-le-lu-jah!
We'll praise the Lord, hal-le-lu - jah! We'll praise the Lord!

Music Arrangement Copyright © 1984 Scripture Union, from *Praise God Together*

Hallelu, hallelu, hallelu, hallelujah;　　We'll praise the Lord, hallelujah!
We'll praise the Lord!　　　　　　　　　We'll praise the Lord, hallelujah!
Hallelu, hallelu, hallelu, hallelujah;　　We'll praise the Lord, hallelujah!
We'll praise the Lord!　　　　　　　　　We'll praise the Lord!

68 Hark, the glad sound

ST. SAVIOUR

Frederick George Baker (1840-1908)

1. Hark, the glad sound! the Saviour comes,
   The Saviour promised long;
   Let ev'ry heart prepare a throne,
   And ev'ry voice a song.

2. He comes, the pris'ners to release
   In Satan's bondage held;
   The chains of sin before Him break,
   The iron fetters yield.

3. He comes the broken heart to bind,
   The wounded soul to cure;
   And with the treasures of His grace
   To enrich the humble poor.

4. Our glad hosannas, Prince of Peace,
   Your welcome shall proclaim;
   And heaven's eternal arches ring
   With Your belovèd name.

Philip Doddridge, 1702-1751
Altered © 1986 Horrobin/Leavers

69 Hark! The herald angels sing

MENDELSSOHN
77 77 D with refrain
Capo 3

Adapted by William Hayman Cummings (1831-1915)
from a chorus of Felix Mendelssohn-Bartholdy (1809-1847)

Hark! The her - ald an-gels sing, "Glo-ry to the new-born King!

Peace on earth, and mer-cy mild, God and sin - ners re-con-ciled."

Joy-ful, all you na-tions, rise,— Join the tri-umph of the skies;

With the an-gel-ic host pro - claim: "Christ is born in Beth-le-hem!"

Hark! the her-ald an-gels sing, "Glo-ry to the new-born King!"

1. Hark! The herald-angels sing,
   "Glory to the new-born King!
   Peace on earth, and mercy mild,
   God and sinners reconciled."
   Joyful, all you nations, rise,
   Join the triumph of the skies;
   With the angelic host proclaim:
   "Christ is born in Bethlehem!"
     Hark! The herald-angels sing,
     "Glory to the new-born King!"

2. Christ, by highest heaven adored,
   Christ, the everlasting Lord,
   Late in time behold Him come,
   Offspring of a virgin's womb!
   Veiled in flesh the Godhead see!
   Hail, the incarnate Deity!
   Pleased as man with men to dwell,
   Jesus, our Immanuel.
     Hark! The herald-angels sing,
     "Glory to the new-born King!"

3. Hail, the heaven-born Prince of Peace!
   Hail, the Sun of Righteousness!
   Light and life to all He brings,
   Risen with healing in His wings.
   Mild He lays His glory by,
   Born that man no more may die;
   Born to raise the sons of earth,
   Born to give them second birth.
     Hark! The herald-angels sing,
     "Glory to the new-born King!"

Charles Wesley, 1707-1788
George Whitfield, 1714-1770
Martin Madan, 1726-1790
and others

70 Happiness is to know the Saviour

Words and music
Ira F. Stanphill

Happiness is to know the Saviour,
Living a life within His favour,
Having a change in my behaviour
Happiness is the Lord.

Real joy is mine, No matter if tear-drops

1. Happiness is to know the Saviour,
   Living a life within His favour,
   Having a change in my behaviour
   Happiness is the Lord.

2. Happiness is a new creation,
   Jesus and me in close relation,
   Having a part in His salvation,
   Happiness is the Lord

   Real joy is mine,
   No matter if teardrops start;
   I've found the secret,
   It's Jesus in my heart!

3. Happiness is to be forgiven,
   Living a life that's worth the living,
   Taking a trip that leads to heaven,
   Happiness is the Lord,
   Happiness is the Lord,
   Happiness is the Lord!

71 Have you heard the raindrops

Words and music
Christian Strover

Capo 3

Joyfully

Have you heard the rain-drops drum-ming on the roof-tops?

Have you heard the rain-drops drip-ping on the ground?

Have you heard the rain-drops splash-ing in the streams And

run-ning to the ri-vers all a-round? *There's wa - ter,*

116

1. Have you heard the raindrops drumming on the rooftops?
   Have you heard the raindrops dripping on the ground?
   Have you heard the raindrops splashing in the streams
   And running to the rivers all around?

   There's water, water of life,
   Jesus gives us the water of life;
   There's water, water of life,
   Jesus gives us the water of life.

2. There's a busy workman digging in the desert,
   Digging with a spade that flashes in the sun;
   Soon there will be water rising in the wellshaft,
   Spilling from the bucket as it comes.
      There's water . . .

3. Nobody can live who hasn't any water,
   When the land is dry then nothing much grows;
   Jesus gives us life if we drink the living water,
   Sing it so that everybody knows.
      There's water . . .

72 Have you seen the pussy cat

Words and Music P. Taylor

Have you seen the pus - sy cat, sit - ting on the wall?

Have you heard his beau-ti-ful purr? *(purr)* Have you seen the li - on

stalk - ing round his prey? Have you heard his ter - ri - ble

roar? *(roar)* One so big, one so small,

Our heaven-ly Fa - ther cares for them all. One so big,

one so small, Our heaven-ly Fa - ther cares.

1. Have you seen the pussy cat, sitting on the wall?
   Have you heard his beautiful purr? *(purr)*
   Have you seen the lion stalking round his prey?
   Have you heard his terrible roar? *(roar)*
   One so big, one so small,
   Our heavenly Father cares for them all.
   One so big, one so small,
   Our heavenly Father cares.

2. Have you seen the children coming home from school?
   Have you heard them shout hurray? *(hurray)*
   Have you seen the grown-ups coming home from work
   Saying 'What a horrible day'? *(what a horrible day)*
   Some so big, some so small,
   Our heavenly Father cares for them all.
   Some so big, some so small,
   Our heavenly Father cares.

73 He brought me to His banqueting house

arr. Phil Burt

He brought me to His ban-queting house and His
ban-ner o-ver me is love He brought me to His
ban-queting house and His ban-ner o-ver me is love He
brought me to His banqueting house and His ban-ner o-ver me is

love His banner ov-er me ___ is love
God loves you and I love you and that's the way it should be.
God loves you and I love you and that's the way it should be.

1. He brought me to His banqueting house, } (3 times)
   And His banner over me is love.
   His banner over me is love.

   God loves you and I love you, and that's the way it should be.
   God loves you and I love you, and that's the way it should be.

2. He feeds me at His banqueting table,
   And His banner over me is love.
   His banner over me is love.
   God loves you . . .

3. He lifts me up to the heavenly places,
   And His banner over me is love.
   His banner over me is love.
   God loves you . . .

4. There's one way to peace through the power of the cross,
   And His banner over me is love.
   His banner over me is love.
   God loves you . . .

5. Jesus is the rock of my salvation,
   And His banner over me is love.
   His banner over me is love.
   God loves you . . .

74 He gave me eyes so I could see

HE MADE ME

Words and music
Alan Pinnock

He gave me eyes so I could see The won-ders of the world. With - out my eyes I could not see The o - ther boys and girls. He gave me ears so I could hear The wind and rain and sea. I've

got to tell it to the world, He made me.

1. He gave me eyes so I could see
   The wonders of the world.
   Without my eyes I could not see
   The other boys and girls.
   He gave me ears so I could hear
   The wind and rain and sea.
   I've got to tell it to the world,
   He made me.

2. He gave me lips so I could speak
   And say what's in my mind.
   Without my lips I could not speak
   A single word or line.
   He made my mind so I could think,
   And choose what I should be.
   I've got to tell it to the world,
   He made me.

3. He gave me hands so I could touch,
   And hold a thousand things.
   I need my hands to help me write,
   To help me fetch and bring.
   These feet he made so I could run,
   He meant me to be free.
   I've got to tell it to the world,
   He made me.

75 He is Lord

Author unknown
arr. Roland Fudge

Arrangement Copyright © 1983 Roland Fudge

1. He is Lord,
   He is Lord,
   He is risen from the dead,
   And He is Lord.
   Ev'ry knee shall bow,
   Ev'ry tongue confess
   That Jesus Christ is Lord.

2. He's my Lord,
   He's my Lord,
   He is risen from the dead,
   And He's my Lord.
   And my knee shall bow,
   And my tongue confess
   That Jesus is my Lord.

Copyright control

76 He made the stars to shine

Words and music
Archie Hall

He made the stars to shine,
He made the rolling sea,
He made the mountains high,
And He made me.

But this is why I love Him,
For me He bled and died,
The Lord of all creation,
Became the crucified.

77 He paid a debt

arr. Phil Burt

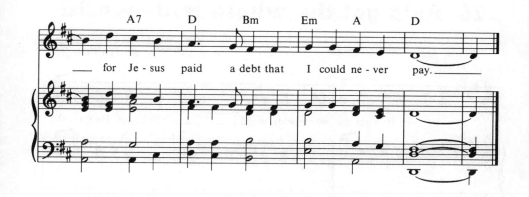

for Je - sus paid a debt that I could ne - ver pay. ____

He paid a debt He did not owe,
I owed a debt I could not pay.
I needed someone to wash my sins away,
And now I sing a brand new song,
Amazing grace the whole day long,
For Jesus paid a debt that I could never pay.

Copyright control

78 He's got the whole wide world

Words and music unknown
arr. Phil Burt

He's got the whole wide world _____ in His hands, He's got the whole wide world _____ in His hands, He's got the whole wide world _____ in His hands, He's got the whole world in His hands. He's got the hands.

1.2.3.

last verse

1. He's got the whole wide world in His hands,
   He's got the whole wide world in His hands,
   He's got the whole wide world in His hands,
   He's got the whole world in His hands.

2. He's got ev'rybody here, in His hands,
   He's got ev'rybody here, in His hands,
   He's got ev'rybody here, in His hands,
   He's got the whole world in His hands.

3. He's got the tiny little baby, in His hands,
   He's got the tiny little baby, in His hands,
   He's got the tiny little baby, in His hands,
   He's got the whole world in His hands.

4. He's got you and me brother, in His hands,
   He's got you and me brother, in His hands,
   He's got you and me brother, in His hands,
   He's got the whole world in His hands.

79 He's Great, He's God

Phil Burt and Greg Leavers

1. He's great! He's God! Jesus Christ is Lord,
   He's great! He's God! Trust His Word.

2. His Word is truth, for He cannot lie;
   His Word is truth to live by.

3. His love is strong and will never end;
   His love is strong. Praise His Name.

4. He lives evermore as the King of kings;
   He lives evermore. Worship Him.

80 He who would valiant be

MONKS GATE 11 11. 12 11.

coll., adpt. and arr. by
Ralph Vaughan Williams (1872-1958)

He____ who would val - iant be 'gainst all dis - as - ter,____ Let____ him in cons - tan - cy fol - low the Mas - ter.____ There's no dis - cour - age - ment shall make him once re -

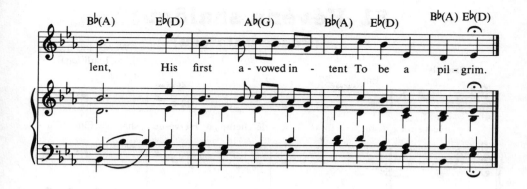

lent,   His   first   a-vowed in - tent To   be   a   pil - grim.

1. He who would valiant be
   'Gainst all disaster,
   Let him in constancy
   Follow the Master.
   There's no discouragement
   Shall make him once relent,
   His first avowed intent
   To be a pilgrim.

2. Who so beset him round
   With dismal stories,
   Do but themselves confound—
   His strength the more is.
   No foes shall stay his might,
   Though he with giants fight:
   He will make good his right
   To be a pilgrim.

3. Since, Lord, You do defend
   Us with Your Spirit,
   We know we at the end
   Shall life inherit.
   Then fancies flee away!
   I'll fear not what men say,
   I'll labour night and day
   To be a pilgrim.

   P. Dearmer, 1867-1936
   after J. Bunyan, 1628-1688

81 Hévénu shalōm
(Peace unto you)

Words and melody
Traditional

Hévénu shalōm aléchem,
Hévénu shalōm aléchem,
Hévénu shalōm aléchem,
Hévénu shalōm, shalōm, shalōm aléchem.

Copyright control

82 How great is our God

Composer unknown
arr. David Peacock

How great is our God! _____ How great is his name! _____
_____ How great is his love, _____ for ev-er the same! _____
_____ He rolled back the wa-ters _____ of the mighty Red Sea,
_____ and He said, 'I'll ne-ver leave you; put your trust in me.'

How great is our God! How great is his name!
How great is his love, for ever the same!
He rolled back the waters of the mighty Red Sea,
And He said, 'I'll never leave you; put your trust in me.'

133

83 How did Moses cross the Red Sea?

arr. Phil Burt

How did Moses cross the Red Sea? How did Moses cross the Red Sea?

How did Moses cross the Red Sea? How did he get a-cross? Did he

swim? No! No! Did he row? No! No! Did he jump? No! No! No!

No! Did he drive? No! No! Did he fly? No! No! How

How did Moses cross the Red Sea?
How did Moses cross the Red Sea?
How did Moses cross the Red Sea?
How did he get across?
Did he swim? No! No!
Did he row? No! No!
Did he jump? No! No! No! No!
Did he drive? No! No!
Did he fly? No! No!
How did he get across?
God blew with His wind, puff, puff, puff, puff.
He blew just enough, 'nough, 'nough, 'nough, 'nough,
And through the sea He made a path,
That's how he got across.

84 How lovely on the mountains
(Our God reigns)

OUR GOD REIGNS

Leonard E. Smith Jnr.

How love-ly on the moun-tains are the feet of Him Who brings good news, good news, Pro-claim-ing peace, an-nounc-ing news of hap-pi-ness, Our God reigns, Our God reigns,

1. How lovely on the mountains are the feet of Him
   Who brings good news, good news,
   Proclaiming peace, announcing news of happiness,
   Our God reigns, our God reigns, our God reigns,
   Our God reigns, our God reigns, our God reigns!

2. You watchmen lift your voices joyfully as one,
   Shout for your King, your King.
   See eye to eye the Lord restoring Zion:
   Your God reigns, your God reigns, your God reigns,
   Your God reigns, your God reigns, your God reigns!

3. Waste places of Jerusalem break forth with joy,
   We are redeemed, redeemed.
   The Lord has saved and comforted His people:
   Your God reigns, your God reigns, your God reigns,
   Your God reigns, your God reigns, your God reigns!

4. Ends of the earth, see the salvation of your God,
   Jesus is Lord, is Lord.
   Before the nations He has bared His holy arm:
   Your God reigns, your God reigns, your God reigns,
   Your God reigns, your God reigns, your God reigns!

85 Hushed was the evening hymn

SAMUEL 66.66.88

A.S. Sullivan (1842-1900)

Hushed was the eve-ning hymn, the tem-ple courts were dark;___ the lamp was burn-ing dim be-fore the sa-cred ark, When sud-den-ly a voice div-ine rang through the sil-ence of the shrine.

1. Hushed was the evening hymn,
   The temple courts were dark;
   The lamp was burning dim
   Before the sacred ark,
   When suddenly a voice divine
   Rang through the silence of the shrine.

2. The old man, meek and mild,
   The priest of Israel, slept;
   His watch the temple child,
   The little Samuel, kept:
   And what from Eli's sense was sealed
   The Lord to Hannah's son revealed.

3. O give me Samuel's ear,
   The open ear, O Lord,
   Alive and quick to hear
   Each whisper of Your word—
   Like him to answer at Your call,
   And to obey You first of all.

4. O give me Samuel's heart,
   A lowly heart, that waits
   To serve and play the part
   You show us at Your gates
   By day and night, a heart that still
   Moves at the breathing of Your will.

5. O give me Samuel's mind,
   A sweet, unmurmuring faith,
   Obedient and resigned
   To You in life and death,
   That I may read with childlike eyes
   Truths that are hidden from the wise.

J.D. Burns, 1823-1864
Altered © 1986 Horrobin/Leavers

86 I am trusting You

BULLINGER 8 5 8 3

E.W. Bullinger (1837-1913)

I am trust-ing You, Lord Je-sus, You have died for me; Trust-ing You for full sal-va-tion Great and free.

1. I am trusting You, Lord Jesus,
   You have died for me;
   Trusting You for full salvation
   Great and free.

2. I am trusting You for pardon—
   At Your feet I bow;
   For Your grace and tender mercy,
   Trusting now.

3. I am trusting You for cleansing,
   Jesus, Son of God;
   Trusting You to make me holy
   By Your blood.

4. I am trusting You to guide me—
   You alone shall lead;
   Every day and hour supplying
   All my need.

5. I am trusting You for power—
   Yours can never fail;
   Words which You yourself shall give me
   Must prevail.

6. I am trusting You, Lord Jesus—
   Never let me fall;
   I am trusting You for ever,
   And for all.

Frances R. Havergal, 1836-1879

87 I am a lighthouse

Words and music
Graham Kendrick
arr. Phil Burt

I am a light - house, a shi-ning and bright house

Out in the waves of a stor-my sea. The oil of the spi - rit

keeps my lamp burn - ing, Je - sus my Lord is the

to Coda

light in me. And when peo - ple see the good

things that I do They'll give prai-ses to God who has

sent us Je-sus. We'll send out a life-boat of

love and for-give-ness and give them a hand to get in.

in. While the storm is rag-ing, whoosh, whoosh, and the

F#m wind is blow-ing, ooo, ooo, and the waves are crash-ing, **B**

D.C. al Coda

crash! crash! crash! crash!

CODA

light in me.

I am a lighthouse, a shining and bright house
Out in the waves of a stormy sea.
The oil of the spirit keeps my lamp burning,
Jesus my Lord is the light in me.
And when people see the good things that I do
They'll give praises to God who has sent us Jesus.
We'll send out a lifeboat of love and forgiveness
And give them a hand to get in.   *(Repeat)*

While the storm is raging, whoosh, whoosh,
And the wind is blowing, ooo, ooo,
And the waves are crashing, crash! crash! crash! crash!

I am a lighthouse, a shining and bright house
Out in the waves of a stormy sea.
The oil of the spirit keeps my lamp burning,
Jesus my Lord is the light in me.

© 1986 G. Kendrick

143

88 I am so glad

P. Bliss (1838-1876)
arr. A.E. Rusbridge (1917-1969)

I AM SO GLAD 10.10.10.10 with chorus

I am so glad that our Fa-ther in heaven

Tells of His love in the book He has given: Won-der-ful things in the

Bi-ble I see; This is the dear-est, that Je-sus loves me.

I am so glad that Je-sus loves me,

144

Je - sus loves me, Je - sus loves me, I am so glad that

Je - sus loves me, Je - sus loves ev - en me.

1. I am so glad that our Father in heaven
   Tells of His love in the book He has given:
   Wonderful things in the Bible I see;
   This is the dearest, that Jesus loves me.

   I am so glad that Jesus loves me,
   Jesus loves me, Jesus loves me,
   I am so glad that Jesus loves me,
   Jesus loves even me.

2. Though I forget Him, and wander away,
   He'll always love me wherever I stray;
   Back to His dear loving arms do I flee,
   When I remember that Jesus loves me.
       I am so glad . . .

3. O if there's only one song I can sing,
   When in His beauty I see the great King,
   This shall my song in eternity be,
   O what a wonder that Jesus loves me
       I am so glad . . .

4. If one should ask of me: How can I tell?
   Glory to Jesus, I know very well;
   God's Holy Spirit with mine does agree,
   Constantly witnessing: Jesus loves me.
       I am so glad . . .

Philipp Bliss, 1838-1876

89 I am the Way, the Truth and the Life

Music traditional
arr. D.J. Crawshaw

I am the Way, the Truth and the Life,

That's what Je - sus said. I am the Way, the Truth and the Life,

That's what Je - sus said. Without the Way there is no

go - ing, Without the truth there is no know-ing, Without the

Life there is no liv - ing, I am the Way, the
Truth and the Life, That's what Je - sus said.

I am the Way, the Truth and the Life,
That's what Jesus said.
I am the Way, the Truth and the Life,
That's what Jesus said.
Without the Way there is no going,
Without the truth there is no knowing,
Without the Life there is no living,
I am the Way, the Truth and the Life,
That's what Jesus said.

Copyright control

90 I can run through a troop

arr. Phil Burt

my sal-va-tion. I can run through a troop And leap ov-er a wall, Hal-le-lu-jah, (Glo-ry, Glo-ry), Hal-le-lu-jah.

I can run through a troop
And leap over a wall,
Hallelujah, (Glory, Glory), Hallelujah,
He's my Prince of Peace,
He gives power to all,
Hallelujah, (Glory, Glory), Hallelujah,
Now there is no condemnation,
Jesus is the rock of my salvation.
I can run through a troop
And leap over a wall,
Hallelujah, (Glory, Glory), Hallelujah.

Copyright control

91 I danced in the morning
(Lord of the dance)

Words and music
Sydney Carter

danced in the morn-ing When the world was be-gun, And I
danced in the moon And the stars___ and the sun, And I
came down from heaven And I danced on the earth At Beth-le-hem I

had my birth. Dance, then, wher-ev-er you may be,

I am the Lord of the Dance, said he, And I'll lead you all, wher-

ev-er you may be, And I'll lead you all in the dance said He.

1. I danced in the morning
   When the world was begun,
   And I danced in the moon
   And the stars and the sun,
   And I came down from heaven
   And I danced on the earth—
   At Bethlehem I had my birth.

   Dance, then, wherever you may be,
   I am the Lord of the Dance, said he,
   And I'll lead you all, wherever you may be,
   And I'll lead you all in the dance, said He.

2. I danced for the scribe
   And the pharisee,
   But they would not dance
   And they wouldn't follow me.
   I danced for the fishermen,
   For James and John—
   They came with me
   And the dance went on.
       Dance, then, wherever . . .

Sydney Carter, b. 1916

151

92 I do not know what lies ahead
(I know who holds the future)

Words and music
Alfred B. Smith and Eugene Clarke

I do not know what lies a-head, The way I can-not see; Yet one stands near to be my guide, He'll show the way to me:

I know who holds the fu-ture, And He'll guide me with His hand, With God things don't just hap-pen, Ev-'ry-thing by Him is planned; So

as I face to-mor-row With its prob-lems large and small, I'll trust the God of mir-a-cles, Give to Him my all.

1. I do not know what lies ahead,
   The way I cannot see;
   Yet one stands near to be my guide,
   He'll show the way to me:

   I know who holds the future,
   And He'll guide me with His hand,
   With God things don't just happen,
   Ev'rything by Him is planned;
   So as I face tomorrow
   With its problems large and small,
   I'll trust the God of miracles,
   Give to Him my all.

2. I do not know how many days
   Of life are mine to spend;
   But one who knows and cares for me
   Will keep me to the end:
       I know who holds . . .

3. I do not know the course ahead,
   What joys and griefs are there;
   But one is near who fully knows,
   I'll trust His loving care:
       I know who holds . . .

93 I'll be still

Music and words
Rick Founds and Todd Collins
arr. Phil Burt

Capo 1

I'll be still and know that You are God;
I'll be still and know You are the Lord;
I'll be still to worship and adore You,
Blessed One, Emmanuel, Jesus.

94 If I were a butterfly

Words and music
Brian Howard

If I were a but-ter-fly,___ I'd thank You Lord for
giv-ing me wings. And if I were a ro-bin in a tree, I'd
thank You Lord that I could sing. And if I were a
fish in the sea, I'd wig-gle my tail and I'd gig-gle with glee, But

I just thank You Fa-ther for mak-ing me 'me'.

For You gave me a heart and You gave me a smile. You

gave me Je-sus and You made me Your child. And I just thank You

Fa-ther for mak-ing me 'me'.

1. If I were a butterfly,
   I'd thank You Lord for giving me wings.
   And if I were a robin in a tree,
   I'd thank You Lord that I could sing.
   And if I were a fish in the sea,
   I'd wiggle my tail and I'd giggle with glee,
   But I just thank You Father for making me 'me'.

   For You gave me a heart
   And You gave me a smile.
   You gave me Jesus and
   You made me Your child.
   And I just thank You Father for making me 'me'.

2. If I were an elephant,
   I'd thank You Lord by raising my trunk.
   And if I were a kangaroo,
   You know I'd hop right up to You.
   And if I were an octopus,
   I'd thank You Lord for my fine looks,
   But I just thank You Father for making me 'me'.
   For You gave me . . .

3. If I were a wiggily worm,
   I'd thank You Lord that I could squirm.
   And if I were a billy goat,
   I'd thank You Lord for my strong throat.
   And if I were a fuzzy wuzzy bear,
   I'd thank You Lord for my fuzzy wuzzy hair,
   But I just thank You Father for making me 'me'.
   For You gave me . . .

                                        Brian Howard

95 If you see someone lying in the road

Words and music
Annie & Neil Simpson

arr. Andy Silver

If you see some-one ly-ing in the road Don't leave him there, give him a hand.___ If you see some-one cry-ing in the road Don't leave him there, give him a hand.___ Does-n't mat-ter ___ who you are; ___ you might be a tramp or a

158

1. If you see someone lying in the road,
   Don't leave him there, give him a hand.
   If you see someone crying in the road
   Don't leave him there, give him a hand.
   Doesn't matter who you are;
   You might be a tramp or a movie-star,
   Just remember whoever you are
   That it's Jesus lying there,
   That it's Jesus crying there.

2. If Jesus sees you lying in the road,
   He won't leave you there, He'll give you a hand.
   If Jesus sees you crying in the road,
   He won't leave you there, He'll give you a hand.
   Doesn't matter who you are;
   You might be a tramp or a movie-star,
   Just remember whoever you are
   That He sees you lying there,
   And He sees you crying there.

96 If you want joy

arr. W.G. Hathaway

If you want joy, real joy, won-der-ful joy, Let Je-sus come in-to your heart. If you want joy, real joy, won-der-ful joy, Let Je-sus come in-to your heart._____ Your sins He'll take a-

If you want joy, real joy, wonderful joy,
Let Jesus come into your heart.
If you want joy, real joy, wonderful joy,
Let Jesus come into your heart.
Your sins He'll take away,
Your night He'll turn to day,
Your heart He'll make over anew,
And then come in to stay.
If you want joy, real joy, wonderful joy,
Let Jesus come into your heart.

161

97 I gotta home in gloryland

arr. Phil Burt

I got-ta home in glo-ry-land that out-shines the sun,

I got-ta home in glo-ry-land that out-shines the sun,

I got-ta home in glo-ry-land that out-shines the sun,____

Way be-yond____ the blue.

1. I gotta home in gloryland that outshines the sun,
   I gotta home in gloryland that outshines the sun,
   I gotta home in gloryland that outshines the sun,
   Way beyond the blue.

   Do Lord, oh do Lord, oh do remember me;
   Do Lord, oh do Lord, oh do remember me;
   Do Lord, oh do Lord, oh do remember me;
   Way beyond the blue.

2. I took Jesus as my saviour, you take Him too . . .

3. If you will not bear a cross, you can't wear a crown . . .

98 I have decided to follow Jesus

arr. Cliff Barrows
and Don Hustad

D.C.

⊕ **CODA**

1. I have decided to follow Jesus,
   I have decided to follow Jesus,
   I have decided to follow Jesus,
   No turning back, no turning back.

2. The world behind me, the cross before me,
   The world behind me, the cross before me,
   The world behind me, the cross before me,
   No turning back, no turning back.

3. Tho' none go with me, I still will follow,
   Tho' none go with me, I still will follow,
   Tho' none go with me, I still will follow,
   No turning back, no turning back.

4. Will you decide now to follow Jesus?
   Will you decide now to follow Jesus?
   Will you decide now to follow Jesus?
   No turning back, no turning back.

99 I have seen the golden sunshine

words and music by
Charlie Chester and
Benny Litchfield

FRIEND OF JESUS, FRIEND OF MINE

I have seen the gol-den sun-shine, I have watched the flow-ers grow, I have
list - ened to the song birds And there's one thing now I know, They were
all put there for us to share By some - one so di - vine, And if
you're a friend of Je - sus, (CLAP CLAP CLAP CLAP) You're a friend of

mine. I've seen the light, I've seen the light, And that's why my heart

sings. I've known the joy, I've known the joy That lov-ing Je-sus brings.

1. I have seen the golden sunshine,
    I have watched the flowers grow,
    I have listened to the song birds
    And there's one thing now I know,
    They were all put there for us to share
    By someone so divine,
    And if you're a friend of Jesus,
    CLAP CLAP CLAP CLAP
    You're a friend of mine.

    I've seen the light, I've seen the light,
    And that's why my heart sings.
    I've known the joy, I've known the joy
    That loving Jesus brings.

2. I have seen the morning sunshine,
    I have heard the oceans roar,
    I have seen the flowers of springtime,
    And there's one thing I am sure,
    They were all put there for us to share
    By someone so divine,
    And if you're a friend of Jesus,
    CLAP CLAP CLAP CLAP
    You're a friend of mine.
    I've seen the light, . . .

100 I hear the sound of the army of the Lord

Dave Moody
arr. R. Fudge

I hear the sound ___ of the ar-my of the Lord,

___ I hear the sound ___ of the

ar-my of the Lord. ___ It's the sound of

praise, It's the sound of ___ war, ___ The

I hear the sound of the army of the Lord,
I hear the sound of the army of the Lord.
It's the sound of praise,
It's the sound of war,
The army of the Lord,
The army of the Lord,
The army of the Lord is marching on.

Dave Moody

101 I may never march in the infantry

arr. Andy Silver

I may never march in the infantry,
Ride with the cavalry, shoot with the artillery,
I may never zoom o'er the enemy,
For I'm in the Lord's army.
I'm in the Lord's army (Yes Sir!)
I'm in the Lord's army (Yes Sir!)
I may never march in the infantry,
Ride with the cavalry, shoot with the artillery,
I may never zoom o'er the enemy,
For I'm in the Lord's army.

102 I met Jesus at the crossroads

arr. Phil Burt

see what He of-fers me, Down here my sins for-giv-en, Up there a home in hea-ven. Praise God! That's the way for me.'

I met Jesus at the crossroads,
Where the two ways meet.
Satan too was standing there,
And he said, 'Come this way,
Lots and lots of pleasures
I can give to you today.'
But I said, 'No, there's Jesus here,
Just see what He offers me,
Down here my sins forgiven,
Up there a home in heaven.
Praise God! That's the way for me.'

Copyright control

103 I met You at the cross

Words by Eric A. Thorn
Music by Roger Jones

I met You at the cross, Je-sus my Lord; I heard You from that cross: My name You called. Asked me to follow You all of my days,

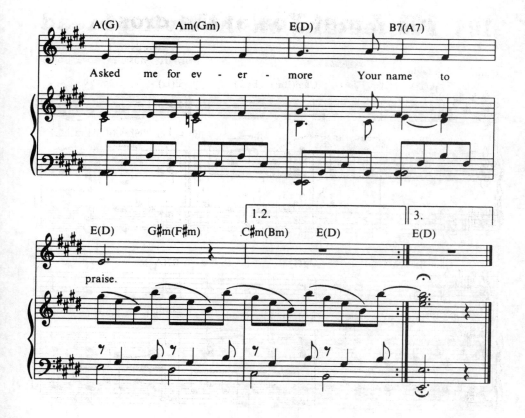

1. I met You at the cross,
   Jesus my Lord;
   I heard You from that cross:
   My name You called—
   Asked me to follow You all of my days,
   Asked me for evermore Your name to praise.

2. I saw You on the cross
   Dying for me;
   I put You on that cross:
   But Your one plea—
   Would I now follow You all of my days,
   And would I evermore Your great name praise?

3. Jesus, my Lord and King,
   Saviour of all,
   Jesus the King of kings,
   You heard my call—
   That I would follow You all of my days,
   And that for evermore Your name I'd praise.

© *Eric A. Thorn*
Christian Music Ministries

104 I'm feeding on the living bread

ne - ver thirst a-gain! No! __ ne - ver thirst a - gain. _____ For
all who drink, so Je - sus said, Will ne-ver, ne-ver thirst a - gain.

I'm feeding on the living bread,
I'm drinking at the fountain head;
For all who drink, so Jesus said,
Will never, never thirst again.
What, never thirst again?
No! never thirst again.
What, never thirst again!
No! never thirst again.
For all who drink, so Jesus said,
Will never, never thirst again.

Altered 1986 Horrobin/Leavers

105 I'm singing for my Lord

Redd Harper

I'm sing-ing for my Lord _____ ev-'ry-where I go, Sing-ing of His wond-rous love that the world may know How He saved a wretch like me by His death on Cal-var-y: I'm sing-ing for my

178

1. I'm singing for my Lord ev'rywhere I go,
   Singing of His wondrous love that the world may know
   How He saved a wretch like me by His death on Calvary:
   I'm singing for my Lord ev'rywhere I go.

2. I'm singing, but sometimes heavy is the rod,
   For this world is not a friend to the grace of God;
   Yet I sing the whole day long, for He fills my heart with song,
   I'm singing for my Lord ev'rywhere I go.

3. I'm singing for the lost just because I know
   Jesus Christ, whose precious blood washes white as snow;
   If my songs to Him can bring some lost soul I'll gladly sing:
   I'm singing for my Lord ev'rywhere I go.

4. I'm singing for the saints as they journey home;
   Soon they'll reach that happy land where they'll never roam,
   And with me they'll join and sing praises to our Lord and King:
   I'm singing for my Lord ev'rywhere I go.

Oswald J. Smith

106 I'm special

Words and music
Graham Kendrick

I'm spe-cial be-cause God has loved me, For He gave the best thing that He had to save me. His own Son Je-sus, cru - ci - fied to take the blame, For all the bad things I have done. Thank you Je-sus, thank you

I'm special because God has loved me,
For He gave the best thing that He had to save me.
His own Son Jesus, crucified to take the blame,
For all the bad things I have done.
Thank you Jesus, thank you Lord,
For loving me so much.
I know I don't deserve anything,
Help me feel your love right now
To know deep in my heart that I'm Your special friend.

107 I'm very glad of God

Words and music
Alice M. Pullen

I'm ve-ry glad of God: His love takes care of me, In ev-ery love-ly thing I see God smiles at me!

1. I'm very glad of God:
   His love takes care of me,
   In every lovely thing I see
   God smiles at me!

2. I'm very glad of God:
   His love takes care of me,
   In every lovely sound I hear
   God speaks to me!

Alice M. Pullen

182

108 In our work and in our play

HARTS

B. Milgrove (1731–1810)

In our work and in our play, Je-sus, ev-er with us stay;

May we serve You all our days, True and faith-ful in our ways.

1. In our work and in our play,
   Jesus, ever with us stay;
   May we serve You all our days,
   True and faithful in our ways.

2. May we in Your strength subdue
   Evil tempers, words untrue,
   Thoughts impure and deeds unkind,
   All things hateful to Your mind.

3. Jesus, from Your throne above,
   Fill anew our hearts with love;
   So that what we say and do
   Shows that we belong to You.

4. Children of the King are we,
   May we loyal to Him be:
   Try to please Him every day,
   In our work and in our play.

W. G. Wills, 1841–1891
Altered © 1986 Horrobin/Leavers

109 In my need Jesus found me

Words and music
Gordon Brattle (1917–1991)

In my need Je-sus found me, Put His
strong arm a-round me, Brought me safe home,
In-to the shel-ter of the fold. _____
Gra-cious Shep-herd that sought me, Pre-cious

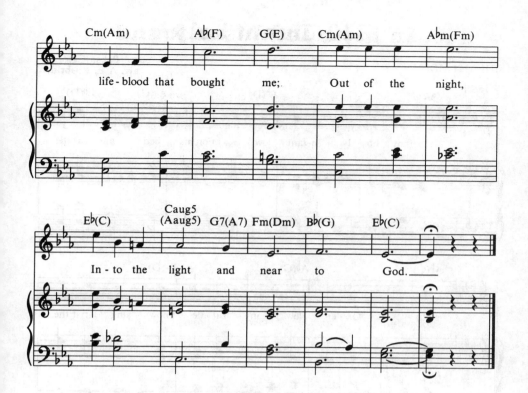

In my need Jesus found me,
Put His strong arm around me,
Brought me safe home,
Into the shelter of the fold.
Gracious Shepherd that sought me,
Precious life-blood that bought me;
Out of the night,
Into the light and near to God.

110 Infant holy

Polish Carol
arr. A.E. Rusbridge

INFANT HOLY

Infant ho-ly, Infant low-ly. For his bed a cat-tle stall; Ox-en low-ing, Lit-tle know-ing Christ the Babe is Lord of all. Swift are wing-ing An-gels sing-ing, Now-ells ring-ing, Ti-dings bring-ing Christ the

Babe is Lord of all. Christ the Babe is Lord of all.

1. Infant holy,
   Infant lowly.
   For his bed a cattle stall;
   Oxen lowing,
   Little knowing
   Christ the Babe is Lord of all.
   Swift are winging
   Angels singing,
   Nowells ringing,
   Tidings bringing,
   Christ the Babe is Lord of all.
   Christ the Babe is Lord of all.

2. Flocks were sleeping,
   Shepherds keeping
   Vigil till the morning new.
   Saw the glory,
   Heard the story,
   Tidings of a gospel true.
   Thus rejoicing,
   Free from sorrow,
   Praises voicing,
   Greet the morrow,
   Christ the Babe was born for you!
   Christ the Babe was born for you!

   tr. E. M.G. Reed
   from the Kingsway Carol Book
   Copyright control

111 In the name of Jesus

Composer unknown
arr. Roland Fudge

Joyfully

In the name of Je-sus, In the name of Je-sus, We have the vic-to-

ry. In the name of Je-sus, In the name of Je-sus,

De-mons will have to flee. Who can tell what

God can do? Who can tell of His love for you?

In the name of Jesus,
In the name of Jesus,
We have the victory.
In the name of Jesus,
In the name of Jesus,
Demons will have to flee.
Who can tell what God can do?
Who can tell of His love for you?
In the name of Jesus, Jesus,
We have the victory.

Copyright control

112 In the stars His handiwork I see

Words and music
Ralph Carmichael
arr. Phil Burt

In the stars His handiwork I see,
On the wind He speaks with majesty;
Though He's ruling over land and sea,
What is that to me?
I will celebrate nativity,
For it has a place in history,
Sure, Christ came to set His people free.
What is that to me?

Then by faith I met Him face to face,
And I felt the wonder of His grace,
Then I knew that He was more than just a God
Who didn't care, who lived away up there.
And now He lives within me day by day,
Ever watching o'er me lest I stray,
Helping me to find the narrow way,
He's ev'rything to me.

113 I serve a risen Saviour

(He lives!)

A.H.A.

Capo 3

A. H. Ackley (1887–1960)

I serve a ris-en Sav-iour, He's in the world to-day; I know that He is liv-ing, What-ev-er men may say; I see His hand of mer-cy, I hear His voice of cheer. And

1. I serve a risen Saviour,
   He's in the world today;
   I know that He is living,
   Whatever men may say;
   I see His hand of mercy,
   I hear His voice of cheer.
   And just the time I need Him
   He's always near.

   He lives, He lives,
   Christ Jesus lives today!
   He walks with me and talks with me
   Along life's narrow way.
   He lives, He lives,
   Salvation to impart!
   You ask me how I know He lives,
   He lives within my heart.

2. In all the world around me
   I see His loving care,
   And tho' my heart grows weary
   I never will despair;
   I know that He is leading,
   Thro' all the stormy blast,
   The day of His appearing
   Will come at last.
      He lives, . . .

3. Rejoice, rejoice, O Christian,
   Lift up your voice and sing
   Eternal hallelujahs
   To Jesus Christ the King!
   The Hope of all who seek Him,
   The Help of all who find,
   None other is so loving,
   So good and kind.
      He lives, . . .

114 Isaiah heard the voice of the Lord

arr. Andy Silver

Lyrics:
I - saiah heard the voice of the Lord And he said, 'Here am I send me.' He loved to do the will of the Lord, so he said, 'Here am I send me; here am I send me; An - y - where for

Isaiah heard the voice of the Lord
And he said, 'Here am I send me.'
He loved to do the will of the Lord, so he said,
'Here am I send me; here am I send me;
Anywhere for Thee.'
So when I hear the voice of the Lord,
I will say, here am I, send me.

115 I sing a song of the saints

GRAND ISLE Irregular

J.H. Hopkins (1861-1945)

I sing a song of the saints of God, Pat-ient and brave and true, Who toiled and fought and lived and died For the Lord they loved and knew. And one was a doc-tor, and one was a queen, And one was a shep-herdess on the green: They were

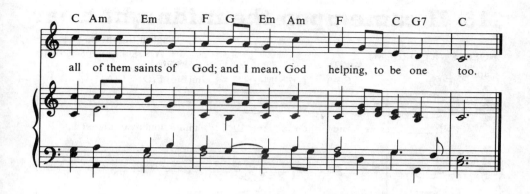

all of them saints of God; and I mean, God helping, to be one too.

1. I sing a song of the saints of God,
   Patient and brave and true,
   Who toiled and fought and lived and died
   For the Lord they loved and knew.
   And one was a doctor, and one was a queen,
   And one was a shepherdess on the green:
   They were all of them saints of God; and I mean,
   God helping, to be one too.

2. They loved their God so good and dear,
   And His love made them strong;
   And they followed the right, for Jesus' sake,
   The whole of their good lives long.
   And one was a soldier, and one was a priest,
   And one was slain by a fierce wild beast:
   And there's not any reason, no, not in the least,
   Why I shouldn't be one too.

3. They lived not only in ages past,
   There are hundreds of thousands still;
   The world is bright with the joyous saints
   Who love to do Jesus' will.
   You can meet them in school, or in lanes, or at sea,
   In church, or in trains, or in shops, or at tea,
   For the saints of God began just like me,
   And I mean to be one too.

© *L. Scott, b. 1898*

116 It came upon the midnight clear

English traditional melody
arr. A.S. Sullivan (1842-1900)

NOEL 8 6 8 6 D (DCM)

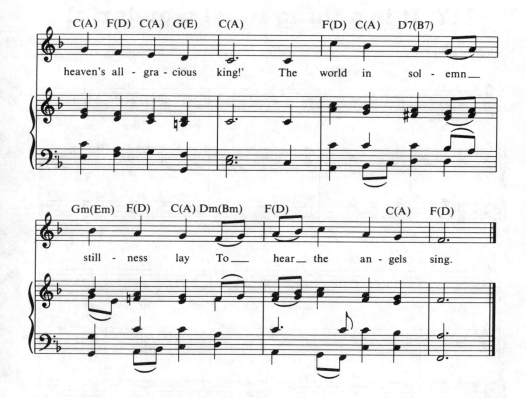

heaven's all - gra - cious king!' The world in sol - emn_ still - ness lay To_ hear_ the an - gels sing.

1. It came upon the midnight clear,
   That glorious song of old,
   From angels bending near the earth
   To touch their harps of gold:
   'Peace on the earth, goodwill to men
   From heaven's all-gracious king!'
   The world in solemn stillness lay
   To hear the angels sing.

2. With sorrow brought by sin and strife
   The world has suffered long
   And, since the angels sang, have passed
   Two thousand years of wrong:
   For man at war with man hears not
   The love-song which they bring:
   O hush the noise, you men of strife,
   And hear the angels sing!

3. And those whose journey now is hard,
   Whose hope is burning low,
   Who tread the rocky path of life
   With painful steps and slow:
   O listen to the news of love
   Which makes the heavens ring!
   O rest beside the weary road
   And hear the angels sing!

4. And still the days are hastening on—
   By prophets seen of old—
   Towards the fulness of the time
   When comes the age foretold:
   Then earth and heaven renewed shall see
   The Prince of Peace, their king;
   And all the world repeat the song
   Which now the angels sing.

E.H. Sears, 1810-1876
© in this version *Jubilate Hymns*

117 It is a thing most wonderful

BROOKFIELD   T.B. Southgate (1814-1868)

It is a thing most won-der-ful

Al - most too won - der - ful to be

That God's own Son should come from heaven

And die to save a child like me.

1. It is a thing most wonderful
   Almost too wonderful to be
   That God's own Son should come from heaven
   And die to save a child like me.

2. And yet I know that it is true
   He came to this poor world below
   And wept and toiled, and mourned and died
   Only because He loved us so.

3. I cannot tell how He could love
   A child so weak and full of sin;
   His love must be so wonderful
   If He could die my love to win.

4. I sometimes think about the cross,
   And shut my eyes, and try to see
   The cruel nails, and crown of thorns,
   And Jesus crucified for me.

5. But, even could I see Him die
   I could but see a little part
   Of that great love which, like a fire,
   Is always burning in His heart.

6. How wonderful it is to know
   His love for me so free and sure;
   But yet more wonderful to see
   My love for Him so faint and poor.

7. And yet I want to love you, Lord:
   O teach me how to grow in grace,
   That I may love you more and more
   Until I see you face to face.

W.W. How, 1823-1897
© in this version *Jubilate Hymns*

118 It's a happy day

Words and music
Gary Pfeiffer

It's a hap-py day ___ and I praise God for the weath - er. ___ It's a hap-py day ___ Liv-ing it for my Lord. It's a hap-py day ___ things are gon - na get bet - ter ___

Liv-ing each day by the prom-is-es in God's Word. _____

Word. _____

1. It's a happy day and I praise God for the weather.
   It's a happy day living it for my Lord.
   It's a happy day things are gonna get better
   Living each day by the promises in God's Word.

2. It's a grumpy day and I can't stand the weather
   It's a grumpy day living it for myself
   It's a grumpy day and things aren't going to get better
   Living each day with my Bible up on my shelf.

3. It's a happy day and I praise God for the weather.
   It's a happy day living it for my Lord.
   It's a happy day things are gonna get better
   Living each day by the promises in God's Word.

Gary Pfeiffer

119 It's me, O Lord

Words and music
Spiritual

It's me, it's me, it's me, O Lord, Stand-in' in the need of prayer. It's me, it's me, it's me, O Lord, Stand-in' in the need of prayer.

Not my bro-ther or my sis-ter, but it's me, O Lord,

Stand-in' in the need of prayer. Not my bro-ther or my sis-ter, but it's

me, O Lord, Stand-in' in the need of prayer.

D.C. al Fine

It's me, it's me, it's me, O Lord,
Standin' in the need of prayer.
It's me, it's me, it's me, O Lord,
Standin' in the need of prayer.

1. Not my brother or my sister, but it's me, O Lord,
   Standin' in the need of prayer.
   Not my brother or my sister, but it's me, O Lord,
   Standin' in the need of prayer.
      It's me, it's me, . . .

2. Not my mother or my father, but it's me, O Lord,
   Standin' in the need of prayer.
   Not my mother or my father, but it's me, O Lord,
   Standin' in the need of prayer.
      It's me, it's me, . . .

3. Not my stranger or my neighbour, but it's me, O Lord,
   Standin' in the need of prayer.
   Not my stranger or my neighbour, but it's me, O Lord,
   Standin' in the need of prayer.
      It's me, it's me, . . .

120 I've got peace like a river

Traditional
arr. Roland Fudge

I've got peace like a ri-ver, Peace like a ri-ver, I've got peace like a ri-ver in my soul, ___ I've got peace like a ri-ver, Peace like a ri-ver, I've got peace like a ri-ver in my soul. ___

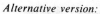

I've got peace like a river,
Peace like a river,
I've got peace like a river
In my soul.
I've got peace like a river,
Peace like a river,
I've got peace like a river,
In my soul.

121 I've got that joy, joy, joy, joy.

Words and music
G. W. Cooke
arr. Phil Burt

heart_____ And I'm so hap-py, so ve-ry hap-py, I've

got the love of Jes-us in my heart. (I've got the heart._____

last time

1. I've got that joy, joy, joy, joy,
   Down in my heart,   (Where?)
   Down in my heart,   (Where?)
   Down in my heart,
   I've got that joy, joy, joy, joy,
   Down in my heart,   (Where?)
   Down in my heart to stay.
     And I'm so happy,
     So very happy,
     I've got the love of Jesus in my heart
     And I'm so happy, so very happy,
     I've got the love of Jesus in my heart

2. I've got the peace that passes understanding
   Down in my heart,   (Where?)
   Down in my heart,   (Where?)
   Down in my heart,
   I've got the peace that passes understanding
   Down in my heart,   (Where?)
   Down in my heart to stay.
     And I'm so happy,
     So very happy,
     I've got the love of Jesus in my heart
     And I'm so happy, so very happy,
     I've got the love of Jesus in my heart

Copyright control

211

122 I want to live for Jesus every day

Anon.
arr. Jeanne Harper

Brightly

I want to live for Je - sus ev' - ry day. (ev' - ry day)

I want to live for Je - sus, come what may. (come what may)

Take the world and all its pleasure, I've got a more en - dur - ing treasure.

I want to live for Je - sus ev' - ry day.

1. I want to live for Jesus ev'ry day. (ev'ry day)
   I want to live for Jesus, come what may. (come what may)
   Take the world and all its pleasure, I've got a more enduring treasure.
   I want to live for Jesus ev'ry day.

2. I'm gonna live for Jesus ev'ry day. (ev'ry day)
   I'm gonna live for Jesus come what may. (come what may)
   Take the world and all its pleasure, I've got a more enduring treasure.
   I'm gonna live for Jesus ev'ry day.

123 I will make you fishers of men

Words and music
Harry D. Clarke

Capo 1

I will make you fishers of men,
Fishers of men, fishers of men;
I will make you fishers of men,
If you follow Me,
If you follow Me, If you follow Me;
I will make you fishers of men,
If you follow Me,

124 I want to walk

C. Simmonds

Music Swiss Folk tune
(*Es Buurebuebli*)
arr. Phil Burt.

I want to walk____ with Je - sus Christ, All the days I live of this life on earth, To give to Him____ com - plete con - trol Of bo - dy and____ of soul:____

Tune for verse and chorus is the same

1. I want to walk with Jesus Christ,
   All the days I live of this life on earth,
   To give to Him complete control
   Of body and of soul:

   Follow Him, follow Him, yield your life to Him,
   He has conquered death, He is King of Kings,
   Accept the joy which He gives to those
   Who yield their lives to Him.

2. I want to learn to speak to Him
   To pray to Him, confess my sin,
   To open my life and let Him in,
   For joy will then be mine:
   Follow Him, follow Him, . . .

3. I want to learn to speak of Him,
   My life must show that He lives in me,
   My deeds, my thoughts, my words must speak
   All of His love for me:
   Follow Him, follow Him, . . .

4. I want to learn to read His Word,
   For this is how I know the way
   To live my life as pleases Him,
   In holiness and joy:
   Follow Him, follow Him, . . .

5. O Holy Spirit of the Lord,
   Enter now into this heart of mine,
   Take full control of my selfish will
   And make me wholly Thine:
   Follow Him, follow Him, . . .

125 I was lost but Jesus found me

Two part round

arr. Phil Burt.

I was lost but Je-sus found me, Found the sheep that went a-

stray. __ Threw His lov - ing arms a - round me, Drew me

back in - to His way *(part 2)* (I was) *Al - le -*

lu - ia, Al - le - lu - ia, Al - le -

1. I was lost but Jesus found me,
   Found the sheep that went astray.
   Threw His loving arms around me,
   Drew me back into His way

   Alleluia, Alleluia,
   Alleluia, Alleluia,
   Alleluia.

2. Glory, glory, alleluia,
   Come and bless the Lord our King,
   Glory, glory, alleluia,
   With His praise all heaven rings.
     Alleluia, Alleluia, . . .

126 I will sing, I will sing

Max Dyer

Liltingly

I will sing, I will sing a song ___ un-to the Lord. I will

sing, I will sing a song ___ un-to the Lord. I will sing, I will sing a song

___ un-to the Lord. Al-le - lu-ia, glo - ry to the Lord. *Al-le -*

lu, alle-lu-ia, glo - ry to the Lord. Alle - lu, alle-lu-ia, glo - ry to the Lord. Alle -

lu, al-le-lu-ia, glo - ry to the Lord. Alle - lu-ia, glo-ry to the Lord.

1. I will sing, I will sing a song unto the Lord.
   I will sing, I will sing a song unto the Lord.
   I will sing, I will sing a song unto the Lord.
   Alleluia, glory to the Lord.

   Allelu, alleluia, glory to the Lord.
   Allelu, alleluia, glory to the Lord.
   Allelu, alleluia, glory to the Lord.
   Alleluia, glory to the Lord.

2. We will come, we will come as one before the Lord.
   We will come, we will come as one before the Lord.
   We will come, we will come as one before the Lord.
   Alleluia, glory to the Lord.
   Allelu, alleluia . . .

3. If the Son, if the Son shall make you free,
   If the Son, if the Son shall make you free,
   If the Son, if the Son shall make you free,
   You shall be free indeed.
   Allelu, alleluia . . .

4. They that sow in tears shall reap in joy,
   They that sow in tears shall reap in joy,
   They that sow in tears shall reap in joy,
   Alleluia, glory to the Lord.
   Allelu, alleluia . . .

5. Ev'ry knee shall bow and ev'ry tongue confess,
   Ev'ry knee shall bow and ev'ry tongue confess,
   Ev'ry knee shall bow and ev'ry tongue confess
   That Jesus Christ is Lord.
   Allelu, alleluia . . .

6. In His name, in His name we have the victory.
   In His name, in His name we have the victory.
   In His name, in His name we have the victory.
   Alleluia, glory to the Lord.
   Allelu, alleluia . . .

Most effective sung unaccompanied,
but with light clapping.
Suggested rhythm:

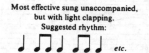 *etc.*

127 I will sing the wondrous story

HYFRYDOL 8 7. 8 7. D

Melody by R. H. Pritchard (1811-1887)

Capo 3

I will sing ___ the won - drous sto - ry
How He left ___ the realms of glo - ry

Of the Christ who died for me,
For the cross on Cal - va - ry.

Yes, I'll sing ___ the won - drous sto - ry

Of the Christ who died for me,

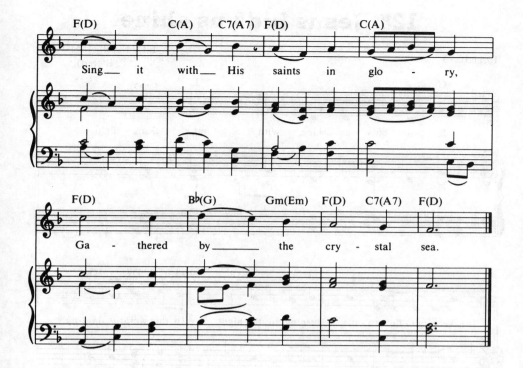

Sing__ it with__ His saints in glo - ry,
Ga - thered by____ the cry - stal sea.

1. I will sing the wondrous story
   Of the Christ who died for me,—
   How He left the realms of glory
   For the cross on Calvary.
   Yes, I'll sing the wondrous story
   Of the Christ who died for me,—
   Sing it with His saints in glory,
   Gathered by the crystal sea.

2. I was lost: but Jesus found me,
   Found the sheep that went astray,
   Raised me up and gently led me
   Back into the narrow way.
   Days of darkness still may meet me;
   Sorrow's path I oft may tread;
   But His presence still is with me,
   By His guiding hand I'm led.

3. He will keep me till the river
   Rolls its waters at my feet:
   Then He'll bear me safely over,
   Made by grace for glory meet.
   Yes, I'll sing the wondrous story
   Of the Christ who died for me,—
   Sing it with His saints in glory,
   Gathered by the crystal sea.

F. H. Rawley 1854–1952

128 Jesus bids us shine

10.11.10.10.

E.O. Excell (1851-1921)
(altered)

1. Jesus bids us shine
   With a pure, clear light,
   Like a little candle
   Burning in the night.
   In this world is darkness;
   So let us shine,
   You in your small corner,
   And I in mine.

2. Jesus bids us shine,
   First of all for Him;
   Well He sees and knows it,
   If our light grows dim.
   He looks down from heaven
   To see us shine,
   You in your small corner,
   And I in mine

3. Jesus bids us shine,
   Then, for all around;
   Many kinds of darkness
   In the world are found—
   Sin, and want and sorrow;
   So we must shine,
   You in your small corner,
   And I in mine.

Susan Warner, 1819-1885

129 Jesus Christ is alive today

Composer unknown
arr. Roland Fudge

Joyfully

Je - sus Christ is a - live to-day, I know, I know it's true.

Sov'reign of the U-ni-verse, I give Him hom-age due.

Seat-ed there at God's right hand, I am with Him in the pro-mised land.

Je - sus lives and reigns in me, That's how I know it's true.

Jesus Christ is alive today,
I know, I know it's true.
Sov'reign of the Universe,
I give Him homage due.

Seated there at God's right hand,
I am with Him in the promised land.
Jesus lives and reigns in me,
That's how I know it's true.

Copyright control

130 Jesus Christ is risen today

EASTER HYMN 7 7 7 7 and Alleluias

Adapted from *Lyra Davidica*, 1708
W. H. Monk (1823–1889)

Suf - fer — to re - deem our loss. — Hal - le - lu - jah!

1. Jesus Christ is risen today, Hallelujah!
   Our triumphant holy day, Hallelujah!
   Who did once, upon the cross, Hallelujah!
   Suffer to redeem our loss. Hallelujah!

2. Hymns of praise then let us sing, Hallelujah!
   Unto Christ, our heavenly King, Hallelujah!
   Who endured the cross and grave, Hallelujah!
   Sinners to redeem and save. Hallelujah!

3. But the pains which He endured, Hallelujah!
   Our salvation have procured, Hallelujah!
   Now in heaven above He's King, Hallelujah!
   Where the angels ever sing Hallelujah!

Lyra Davidica, 1708

131 Jesus Christ the Lord is born

PUER NOBIS

German Carol Melody
harm. Geoffrey Shaw (d. 1943)

Je - sus Christ the Lord is born, All the bells are ring - ing! An - gels greet the ho - ly One and shepherds hear them sing - ing, and shep - herds hear them sing - ing:

From *The Oxford Book of Carols*, by permission of Oxford University Press

1. Jesus Christ the Lord is born,
All the bells are ringing!
Angels greet the holy One
And shepherds hear them singing,
And shepherds hear them singing:

2. 'Go to Bethlehem today,
Find your King and Saviour:
Glory be to God on high,
To earth his peace and favour,
To earth his peace and favour!'

3. Held within a cattle stall,
Loved by love maternal,
See the master of us all,
Our Lord of lords eternal,
Our Lord of lords eternal!

4. Soon shall come the wise men three,
Rousing Herod's anger;
Mother's hearts shall broken be
And Mary's son in danger,
And Mary's son in danger.

5. Death from life and life from death,
Our salvation's story:
Let all living things give breath
To Christmas songs of glory,
To Christmas songs of glory!

After German authors (from the fifteenth century)
© *Michael Perry, / Jubilee Hymns*

132 Jesus died for all the children

Jesus died for all the children,
All the children of the world;
Red and yellow, black and white,
All are precious in His sight:
Jesus died for all the children of the world.

133 Jesus, how lovely You are

Dave Bolton

Je - sus,___ how love-ly You are!___

You are so gen - tle so pure and kind, You___ shine like the

morn - ing star: Je - sus___ how love-ly You are.___

Al - le - lu - ia, Je - sus is

Words and music © 1975 Kingsway's Thankyou Music,
P O Box 75, Eastbourne, East Sussex BN23 6NW

my Lord _ and King. Al - le - lu - ia,

Je - sus is my ev - ry - thing.

Jesus, how lovely You are!
You are so gentle so pure and kind,
You shine like the morning star:
Jesus how lovely You are.

1. Alleluia, Jesus is my Lord and King.
   Alleluia, Jesus is my everything.
       Jesus, how lovely . . .

2. Alleluia, Jesus died and rose again;
   Alleluia, Jesus forgave all my sin.
       Jesus, how lovely . . .

3. Alleluia, Jesus is meek and lowly;
   Alleluia, Jesus is pure and holy.
       Jesus, how lovely . . .

4. Alleluia, Jesus is the bridegroom;
   Alleluia, Jesus will take His bride soon.
       Jesus, how lovely . . .

134 Jesus' hands were kind hands

Margaret Cropper (adapted)

French Melody, arr. J.W.

Jesus' hands were kind hands doing good to all,
Healing pain and sickness, blessing children small.
And my hands should serve Him, ready at His call.
Jesus' hands were kind hands doing good to all.

© *Stainer and Bell Ltd*

135 Jesus is knocking

Words and music
Gordon Brattle (1917–1991)

Capo 3

Je - sus is knock - ing, pa - tient - ly wait - ing,

Out - side your heart's closed door. _____

Do not re - ject Him, sim - ply ac - cept Him,

Now and for - ev - er more. _____

Jesus is knocking, patiently waiting,
Outside your heart's closed door.
Do not reject Him, simply accept Him,
Now and forever more.

136 Jesus is a friend of mine

Paul Mazak
arr. Judith Barnard

1. Jesus is a friend of mine
   Praise Him!
   Jesus is a friend of mine
   Praise Him!
   Praise Him! Praise Him!
   Jesus is a friend of mine
   Praise Him!

2. Jesus died to set us free
   Praise Him!
   Jesus died to set us free
   Praise Him!
   Praise Him! Praise Him!
   Jesus died to set us free
   Praise Him!

3. Jesus is the King of Kings
   Praise Him!
   Jesus is the King of Kings
   Praise Him!
   Praise Him! Praise Him!
   Jesus is the King of Kings
   Praise Him!

137 Jesus is Lord!

David J. Mansell

Capo 1

With majesty

Je - sus is Lord! Cre - a - tion's voice pro - claims it,

For by his power each tree and flower was planned and made

Je - sus is Lord! The u - ni - verse de - clares it.

Sun, moon and stars in hea - ven cry Je - sus is Lord!

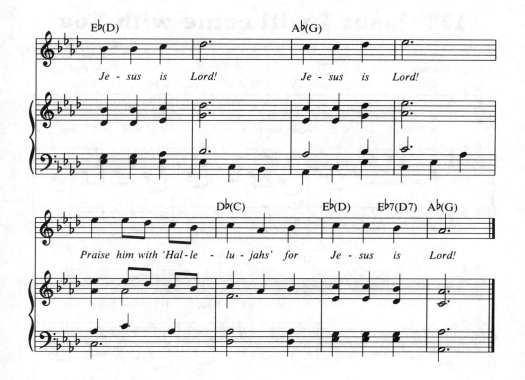

1. Jesus is Lord! Creation's voice proclaims it,
   For by his power each tree and flower was planned and made
   Jesus is Lord! The universe declares it.
   Sun, moon and stars in heaven cry Jesus is Lord!

   Jesus is Lord! Jesus is Lord!
   Praise Him with 'Hallelujahs' for Jesus is Lord!

2. Jesus is Lord! Yet from his throne eternal
   In flesh He came to die in pain on Calv'ry's tree.
   Jesus is Lord! From Him all life proceeding,
   Yet gave his life a ransom thus setting us free.
       Jesus is Lord! . . .

3. Jesus is Lord! O'er sin the mighty conqueror,
   From death He rose and all his foes shall own his name.
   Jesus is Lord! God sends his Holy Spirit
   To show by works of power that Jesus is Lord.
       Jesus is Lord! . . .

138 Jesus I will come with You

Words and music
Roger Jones
arr. Phil Burt

(2–Part Round)

Je - sus I will come with You, I will fol - low
in Your way. I will trust You, I will bring You
all I have to - day. *2nd part starts here* Je - sus, -
You're the Way, Je - sus, You're the Truth,

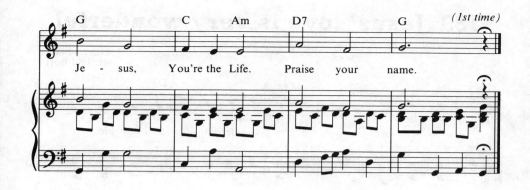

Je - sus, You're the Life. Praise your name.

Jesus I will come with You,
I will follow in Your way.
I will trust You,
I will bring You all I have today.
Jesus, You're the Way,
Jesus, You're the Truth,
Jesus, You're the Life.
Praise Your name.

139 Jesus' love is very wonderful

Music traditional
arr. Phil Burt

Je-sus' love is ve-ry won-der-ful, Je-sus' love is

ve-ry won-der-ful, Je-sus' love is ve-ry won-der-ful,

O won-der-ful love! So high, you

can't get o-ver it, So low, you can't get un-der it,

So wide, you can't get round it, O won-der-ful love!

Jesus' love is very wonderful,
Jesus' love is very wonderful,
Jesus' love is very wonderful,
O wonderful love!
So high, you can't get over it,
So low, you can't get under it,
So wide, you can't get round it,
O wonderful love!

H. W. Rattle
© *Scripture Union*

140 Jesus loves me!

77.77 with chorus

W. B. Bradbury (1816-1868)

Capo 1

Yes! Je - sus loves me! The Bi - ble tells me so.

1. Jesus loves me! this I know,
   For the Bible tells me so;
   Little ones to Him belong;
   They are weak, but He is strong.

   Yes! Jesus loves me!
   Yes! Jesus loves me!
   Yes! Jesus loves me!
   The Bible tells me so.

2. Jesus loves me! He who died
   Heaven's gate to open wide;
   He will wash away my sin;
   Let His little child come in.
      Yes! Jesus loves me! . . .

3. Jesus loves me! He will stay
   Close beside me all the way;
   Then His little child will take
   Up to heaven, for His dear sake.
      Yes! Jesus loves me! . . .

Anna Warner, 1827-1915

141 Jesus, Name above all names

Words and music
Naida Hearn
arr. Roland Fudge

Slow and gentle

Je - sus, Name a - bove all names. Beau - ti - ful Sav - iour, Glor - i - ous Lord, Em - man - u - el, God is with us, Bless - ed Re -

Jesus, Name above all names.
Beautiful Saviour,
Glorious Lord, Emmanuel,
God is with us,
Blessed Redeemer,
Living Word.

142 Jesus said whosoever will

arr. Andy Silver

1. Jesus said that whosoever will,
   Whosoever will, whosoever will.
   Jesus said that whosoever will,
   Whosoever will may come.

2. I'm so glad that He included me,
   He included me, He included me.
   I'm so glad that He included me,
   When Jesus said that whosoever will may come.

Copyright control

143 Joshua fit the battle of Jericho

Words and music
Spiritual

none like good old Jos-hua At the bat-tle of Je - ri -

1.2. cho. (Up) down, that morn-ing. *Joshua fit the bat-tle of*___

3.

*Je - ri - cho,*___ *Je - ri - cho,*___ *Je - ri - cho,*___

*Joshua fit the battle of*___ *Je - ri - cho, And the walls came tumbling down.*

Joshua fit the battle of Jericho,
Jericho, Jericho,
Joshua fit the battle of Jericho,
And the walls came tumbling down.

1. You may talk about your king of Gideon,
   You may talk about your man of Saul,
   But there's none like good old Joshua
   At the battle of Jericho.

2. Up to the walls of Jericho
   He marched with spear in hand.
   'Go blow them ram-horns,' Joshua cried,
   'Cause the battle am in my hand.'

3. Then the ram-sheeps' horns began to blow,
   Trumpets began to sound.
   Joshua commanded the children to shout,
   And the walls came tumbling down, that morning.

Joshua fit the battle of Jericho,
Jericho, Jericho,
Joshua fit the battle of Jericho,
And the walls came tumbling down.

144 Joy is the flag

Composer unknown
arr. E.J. Hume

Joy is the flag flown high from the cas-tle of my heart, From the cas-tle of my heart, from the cas-tle of my heart. Joy is the flag flown high from the cas-tle of my heart, When the King is in res-id-ence there. ___ So let it fly in the sky, let the

whole world know, let the whole world know, let the

whole world know. So let it fly in the sky, let the

whole world know, That the King is in res-id-ence there.____

Joy is the flag flown high from the castle of my heart,
From the castle of my heart, from the castle of my heart.
Joy is the flag flown high from the castle of my heart,
When the King is in residence there.

So let it fly in the sky, let the whole world know,
Let the whole world know, let the whole world know.
So let it fly in the sky, let the whole world know,
That the King is in residence there.

Copyright control

145 Jubilate, everybody

F. Dunn

Lyrics:

Ju-bi-la-te, ev-'ry-bo-dy, Serve the Lord in all your ways, And come before his pre-sence singing; En-ter now his courts with praise. For the Lord our God is gracious, and His mer-cy ev-er-last-ing.

Jubilate, ev'rybody,
Serve the Lord in all your ways,
And come before His presence singing;
Enter now His courts with praise.
For the Lord our God is gracious,
And His mercy everlasting.
Jubilate, jubilate,
Jubilate Deo!

146 Just as I am

JUST AS I AM 888.6

Joseph Barnaby (1838-1896)

Capo 1

Just as I am, Your child to be,
Friend of the young, who died for me;
To give my life whole-heart-ed-ly,
O Je-sus Christ I come.

1. Just as I am, Your child to be,
   Friend of the young, who died for me;
   To give my life wholeheartedly,
   O Jesus Christ I come.

2. While I am still a child today,
   I give my life, my work and play
   To Him alone, without delay,
   With all my heart I come.

3. I see in Jesus Christ the light,
   With Him as Lord, and in His might
   I turn from sin to what is right,
   My Lord to You I come.

4. Lord, take my dreams of fame and gold,
   I accept now a life controlled
   By faith in You as days unfold,
   With my whole life I come.

5. Just as I am, young, strong and free,
   To be the best that I can be,
   That others may see You in me,
   Lord of my life I come.

Marianne Farningham, 1834-1909
Altered © 1986 Horrobin/Leavers

147 Keep me shining, Lord

Words and music
K.B. Wilkinson (1859-1928)

Keep me shining, Lord,
Keep me shining, Lord,
In all I say and do;
That the world may see
Christ lives in me,
And learn to love Him too.

148 King of Kings

Sophie Conty and Naomi Batya

Music: Ancient Hebrew Folksong

Lively

King of Kings and Lord of ___ Lords, Glo-ry, hal-le-lu-jah!

King of Kings and Lord of ___ Lords, Glo-ry, hal-le-lu-jah! Jesus, Prince of Peace,

Glo-ry, hal-le-lu-jah! Je-sus, Prince of Peace, Glo-ry, hal-le-lu-jah!

King of Kings and Lord of Lords,
Glory, hallelujah!
King of Kings and Lord of Lords,
Glory, hallelujah!
Jesus, Prince of Peace,
Glory, hallelujah!
Jesus, Prince of Peace,
Glory, hallelujah!

Sophie Conty and Naomi Batya

149 Kum ba yah

Words and music
Traditional

Kum ba yah, my Lord, _____ Kum ba yah. _____ Kum ba
yah, my Lord, Kum ba yah. _____ Kum ba yah, my Lord,
_____ Kum ba yah. _____ O Lord, ___ Kum ba yah.

1. Kum ba yah, my Lord, Kum ba yah.
   Kum ba yah, my Lord, Kum ba yah.
   Kum ba yah, my Lord, Kum ba yah.
   O Lord, Kum ba yah.

2. Someone's crying Lord, Kum ba yah..
   Someone's crying Lord, Kum ba yah.
   Someone's crying Lord, Kum ba yah.
   O Lord, Kum ba yah.

3. Someone's singing Lord, Kum ba yah.
   Someone's singing Lord, Kum ba yah.
   Someone's singing Lord, Kum ba yah.
   O Lord, Kum ba yah.

4. Someone's praying Lord, Kum ba yah.
   Someone's praying Lord, Kum ba yah.
   Someone's praying Lord, Kum ba yah.
   O Lord, Kum ba yah.

5. Hear our prayer, O Lord, hear our prayer,
   Keep our friends, O Lord, in Your care;
   Keep our friends, O Lord, in Your care.
   O Lord, Kum ba yah.

150 Let's talk about Jesus

Words and music
H. Buffum, Jr.

Let's talk about Jesus, the King of kings is He,
The Lord of lords supreme, thro' all eternity.
The Great I AM, the Way, the Truth, the Life, the Door.
Let's talk about Jesus more and more.

151 Led like a lamb
(You're alive)

Graham Kendrick

Steady

Led like a lamb to the slaugh - ter in si-lence and shame There on Your back You carr - ied a world Of vio-lence and pain Bleed-ing, dy-ing,

* The word "Alleluia" can be sung antiphonally, as indicated, the people having been divided into three equal groups.

1. Led like a lamb   *You're alive*   2. At break of dawn   3. At the right hand
   To the slaughter   *You're alive*   Poor Mary   Of the Father
   In silence and shame   *You have risen!*   Still weeping she came   Now seated on high
   There on Your back   *Alleluia*   When through her grief   You have begun
   You carried a world   *And the power*   She heard Your voice   Your eternal reign
   Of violence and pain   *And the glory*   Now speaking her name   Of justice and joy
   Bleeding, dying,   *Is given*   Mary, Master,   Glory, glory,
   Bleeding, dying.   *Alleluia*   Mary, Master.   Glory, glory.
                            Jesus to You.   *You're alive . . .*   *You're alive . . .*

259

152 Let us praise God together

J.E. Seddon

Calhoun Melody
arr. D.G. Wilson

praise, His___ name be ex - al - ted on high.___

1. Let us praise God together,
   Let us praise,
   Let us praise God together,
   Him proclaim.
   He is faithful in all His ways,
   He is worthy of all our praise,
   His Name be exalted on high.

2. Let us seek God together,
   Let us pray,
   Let us seek His forgiveness
   As we pray.
   He will cleanse us from all sin,
   He will help us the fight to win,
   His Name be exalted on high.

3. Let us serve God together,
   Let us serve;
   Let our lives show His goodness
   As we work.
   Christ the Lord is the world's true light,
   Let us serve Him with all our might;
   His Name be exalted on high.

J.E. Seddon
© 1969 Mrs Mavis Seddon / Jubilate Hymns

153 Live, live, live

Words and music
Marcus Uzilevsky

Live, live, live, Live, live, live, Je-sus is liv-ing in my

soul._____ Live, live, live, Live, live, live,

Je-sus is liv-ing in my soul.

Hang-ing on the tree,_____ He prayed for you and me.

Live, live, live,
Live, live, live,
Jesus is living in my soul.
Live, live, live,
Live, live, live,
Jesus is living in my soul.

1. Hanging on the tree,
   He prayed for you and me.
   Jesus is living in my soul.
   To His spirit yield,
   By His stripes we're healed.
   Jesus is living in my soul.
      Live, live, live . . .

2. He took me out of darkness,
   And He set me free.
   Jesus is living in my soul.
   Once I was blind,
   Now I can see.
   Jesus is living in my soul.
      Live, live, live . . .

3. Gonna shout and sing,
   Let the hallelujah ring.
   Jesus is living in my soul.
   I'm gonna shout and sing,
   There's healing in His wing.
   Jesus is living in my soul.
      Live, live, live . . .

154 Let us with a gladsome mind

MONKLAND

John Antes (1840–1811)
arr. Douglas Coombes

Moderately fast

Let us with a glad-some mind Praise the Lord, for He is kind:

For His mer-cies still en-dure, Ev - er faith-ful, ev-er sure.

Music arrangement © Douglas Coombes/Lindsay Music

1. Let us with a gladsome mind
Praise the Lord, for He is kind:

   For His mercies still endure,
   Ever faithful, ever sure.

2. He, with all-commanding might,
Filled the new-made world with light:
   For His mercies . . .

3. All things living He does feed,
His full hand supplies their need:
   For His mercies . . .

4. Let us then, with gladsome mind
Praise the Lord, for He is kind:
   For His mercies . . .

John Milton, 1608–1674

264

155 Lord dismiss us

DISMISSAL 87.87.87

W.L. Viner (1790-1867)

Lord dis-miss us with Your bless-ing, Fill our hearts with joy and peace.

Let us each, Your love pos-sess-ing, Tri - umph in re - deem-ing grace;

O re - fresh us, O re-fresh us As to_ serve we leave this place.

1. Lord dismiss us with Your blessing,
   Fill our hearts with joy and peace.
   Let us each, Your love possessing,
   Triumph in redeeming grace;
   O refresh us, O refresh us
   As to serve we leave this place.

2. Thanks we give and adoration,
   For Your gospel's joyful sound;
   May the fruits of Your salvation
   In our hearts and lives abound;
   So Your presence, so Your presence
   Will with us always be found.

John Fawcett, 1740-1817
Altered © 1986 Horrobin/Leavers

156 Lord Jesus Christ

LIVING LORD

Words and music
Patrick Appleford (b. 1925)

Lord Jesus Christ, You have come to us, You are one with us, Mary's Son. Cleansing our souls from all their sin, Pouring Your love and goodness in, Jesus, our love for You we sing,

Verse 2 should only be sung when Holy Communion is being celebrated.

1. Lord Jesus Christ,
   You have come to us,
   You are one with us,
   Mary's Son.
   Cleansing our souls from all their sin,
   Pouring Your love and goodness in,
   Jesus, our love for You we sing,
   Living Lord.

2. Lord Jesus Christ,
   Now and every day
   Teach us how to pray,
   Son of God.
   You have commanded us to do
   This, in remembrance, Lord, of You:
   Into our lives Your power breaks through,
   Living Lord.

3. Lord Jesus Christ,
   You have come to us,
   Born as one of us,
   Mary's Son.
   Led out to die on Calvary,
   Risen from death to set us free,
   Living Lord Jesus, help us see
   You are Lord.

4. Lord Jesus Christ,
   I would come to You,
   Live my life for You,
   Son of God.
   All Your commands I know are true,
   Your many gifts will make me new,
   Into my life Your power breaks through,
   Living Lord.

Patrick Appleford, b. 1925

157 Lord of all hopefulness

SLANE

harm. M. Shaw (1875-1958)

Lord of all__ hope-ful-ness, Lord of all joy, Whose trust, ev-er child-like, no cares could des-troy, Be there at__ our__ wak-ing, and give us, we pray, Your peace in our hearts, Lord, at the break of the day.

1. Lord of all hopefulness, Lord of all joy,
   Whose trust, ever child-like, no cares could destroy,
   Be there at our waking, and give us, we pray,
   Your peace in our hearts, Lord, at the break of the day.

2. Lord of all eagerness, Lord of all faith,
   Whose strong hands were skilled at the plane and the lathe,
   Be there at our labours, and give us, we pray,
   Your strength in our hearts, Lord, at the noon of the day.

3. Lord of all kindliness, Lord of all grace,
   Your hands swift to welcome, Your arms to embrace,
   Be there at our homing, and give us, we pray,
   Your love in our hearts, Lord, at the eve of the day.

4. Lord of all gentleness, Lord of all calm,
   Whose voice is contentment, whose presence is balm,
   Be there at our sleeping, and give us, we pray,
   Your peace in our hearts, Lord, at the end of the day.

Jan Struther, d. 1953

158 Love, joy, peace and patience

FRUITS OF THE SPIRIT

Words and music
Andy Silver

Love, joy, peace and pa - tience, kind - ness, good - ness, meek - ness, faith, self-con - trol. These are the fruit of God's Ho - ly Spi - rit and a - gainst such there is no Law. Those who be - long to Christ

Love, joy, peace and patience, kindness,
Goodness, meekness, faith, self-control.
These are the fruit of God's Holy Spirit
And against such there is no Law.
Those who belong to Christ should now live this way,
Walking in the Spirit each day.
So praise Him, praise Him, give Him all the glory,
Walking in the Spirit each day.

159 Low in the grave He lay

CHRIST AROSE 6.5.6.4 and chorus

R. Lowry (1826-1899)

Capo 1

Low in the grave He lay, Je-sus, my Sav-iour;

Wait-ing the com-ing day, Je-sus, my Lord.

Up from the grave He a-rose, With a migh-ty tri-umph o'er His

foes; He a-rose a Vic-tor from the dark do-main, And He

lives for ev - er with His saints to reign: He a - rose! He a -
rose! Hal - le - lu - jah! Christ a - rose!

1. Low in the grave He lay,
   Jesus, my Saviour;
   Waiting the coming day,
   Jesus, my Lord.

   Up from the grave He arose,
   With a mighty triumph o'er His foes;
   He arose a Victor from the dark domain,
   And He lives for ever with His saints to reign:
   He arose! He arose! Hallelujah! Christ arose!

2. Vainly they watch His bed,
   Jesus, my Saviour;
   Vainly they seal the dead,
   Jesus, my Lord.
      Up from the grave . . .

3. Death cannot keep his prey,
   Jesus my Saviour;
   He tore the bars away,
   Jesus, my Lord.
      Up from the grave . . .

Robert Lowry, 1826-1899

273

160 Majesty

Jack W. Hayford

So ex - alt, lift up on high, the name of Je - sus___ Mag - ni -
fy, come glo - ri - fy, Christ Je - sus the King.___
Maj - es - ty,___ worship His Maj - es - ty___ Je - sus who
died, now glo - ri - fied, King of all kings.___

Majesty, worship His Majesty;
Unto Jesus be glory, honour and praise.
Majesty, kingdom authority, flows from His throne
Unto His own, His anthem raise.
So exalt, lift up on high, the name of Jesus
Magnify, come glorify, Christ Jesus the King.
Majesty, worship His Majesty
Jesus who died, now glorified, King of all kings.

161 Make me a channel of Your peace

PRAYER OF ST. FRANCIS

Sebastian Temple
arr. Betty Pulkingham

Make me a chan-nel of Your peace. Where there is hat-red let me bring Your love; Where there is in-jur-y, Your par-don, Lord; And where there's doubt, true faith in You. Oh,

Mas-ter, grant that I may nev-er seek _____ So much to be con-soled as to con-sole; _____ To be un-der-stood as to un-der-stand; _____ To be loved, as to love with all my soul. _____

1. Make me a channel of Your peace.
   Where there is hatred let me bring Your love;
   Where there is injury, Your pardon, Lord;
   And where there's doubt, true faith in You.

   Oh, Master, grant that I may never seek
   So much to be consoled as to console;
   To be understood as to understand;
   To be loved, as to love with all my soul.

2. Make me a channel of Your peace.
   Where there's despair in life let me bring hope;
   Where there is darkness, only light;
   And where there's sadness, ever joy.
       Oh, Master, . . .

3. Make me a channel of Your peace.
   It is in pardoning that we are pardoned,
   In giving to all men that we receive;
   And in dying that we're born to eternal life.

277

162 Make me a servant

Words and music
Kelly Willard

Sustained

G   Em7   Am7   D7sus   D7

Make me a ser-vant, hum-ble and meek,

Am7   D7sus   D7   C   G   C   G   B7

Lord, let me lift up those who are___ weak.

Em   Em   Em   Cm

And may the prayer of my heart al-ways be:

G   Am7   G   C

Make me a ser-vant, make me a ser-vant,

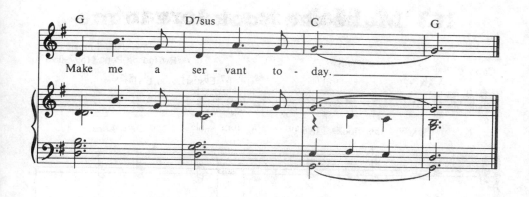

Make me a ser - vant to - day. _____

Make me a servant, humble and meek,
Lord, let me lift up those who are weak.
And may the prayer of my heart always be:
Make me a servant, make me a servant,
Make me a servant today.

163 Make the Book live to me

Words and music
R. Hudson Pope (1897–1967)

Make the Book live to me, O Lord,
Show me Yourself within Your Word,
Show me myself and show me my Saviour, And make the Book live to me.

Make the Book live to me, O Lord,
Show me Yourself within Your Word,
Show me myself and show me my Saviour,
And make the Book live to me.

164 Mary had a little baby

Words and music
Andy Silver

Mary had a little baby, Mary had a little baby; Here and there and eve-ry-where the an-gels sang Praise the Lord. Mary had a lit-tle ba-by, Mary had a lit-tle ba-by;

Here and there and eve-ry-where the an-gels sang Praise the Lord.

Glo-ry, glo-ry, glo-ry, glo-ry, Eve-ry-bo-dy sing the song.

Glo-ry, glo-ry, glo-ry, glo-ry, God's

Son has come to earth. Ma-ry

had a lit-tle ba-by, __ Ma __ ry __ had a lit-tle ba-by; __

Here and there and eve-ry-where the an-gels sang Praise the Lord. _____

Mary had a little baby, Mary had a little baby;
Here and there and everywhere the angels sang
Praise the Lord.
Mary had a little baby, Mary had a little baby;
Here and there and everywhere the angels sang
Praise the Lord.

Glory, glory, glory, glory,
Everybody sing the song.
Glory, glory, glory, glory,
God's Son has come to earth.

Mary had a little baby, Mary had a little baby;
Here and there and everywhere the angels sang
Praise the Lord.

165 May the mind of Christ my Saviour

ST. LEONARDS 87.85

Capo 1

A.C. Barham Gould (1891-1953)

1. May the mind of Christ my Saviour
   Live in me from day to day,
   By His love and power controlling
   All I do or say.

2. May the word of God dwell richly
   In my heart from hour to hour,
   So that all may see I triumph
   Only through His power.

3. May the peace of God my Father
   Rule my life in everything,
   That I may be calm to comfort
   Sick and sorrowing.

4. May the love of Jesus fill me,
   As the waters fill the sea;
   Him uplifting, self-denying,
   This is victory.

5. May I run the race before me,
   Strong and brave onward I go,
   Looking only unto Jesus
   As in Him I grow.

Kate B. Wilkinson, 1859–1928
Copyright control

166 Morning has broken

BUNESSAN

Old Gaelic melody

1. Morning has broken
   Like the first morning,
   Blackbird has spoken
   Like the first bird.
   Praise for the singing!
   Praise for the morning!
   Praise for them, springing
   Fresh from the Lord!

2. Mine is the sunlight!
   Mine is the morning
   Here in the bright light
   Of this fair day!
   Praise with elation,
   Praise every morning
   God's re-creation
   Of the new day!

167 Mister Noah built an ark

arr. Phil Burt

Down came the rain in tor-rents, And on-ly eight were saved.

1. Mister Noah built an ark,
   The people thought it such a lark,
   Mister Noah pleaded so
   But into the ark they would not go.

   Down came the rain in torrents,   (splish, splash) ⎫
   Down came the rain in torrents,   (splish, splash) ⎬ **spoken**
   Down came the rain in torrents, ⎭
   And only eight were saved.

2. The animals went in two by two,
   Elephant, giraffe and kangaroo.
   All were safely stowed away
   On that great and awful day.

   Down came the rain in torrents,   (splish, splash) ⎫
   Down came the rain in torrents,   (splish, splash) ⎬ **spoken**
   Down came the rain in torrents, ⎭
   And only eight were saved.

   (Then to tune of chorus)

   Whenever you see a rainbow,
   Whenever you see a rainbow,
   Whenever you see a rainbow,
   Remember God is love.

168 My faith is like a staff of oak

8.6.8.6.888.6.

Capo 1

Traditional Swiss melody

My faith is like a staff of oak, The
tra-vel-ler's well-loved aid; My faith, it is a
wea-pon strong, The sol-dier's trus-ty
blade. I'll tra-vel on, and still be stirred To

act - ion at___ my___ Mas - ter's word; By all life's pe - rils___ un - de - terred, A sol - dier___ un - a - fraid.

1. My faith is like a staff of oak,
   The traveller's well-loved aid;
   My faith, it is a weapon strong,
   The soldier's trusty blade.
   I'll travel on, and still be stirred
   To action at my Master's word;
   By all life's perils undeterred,
   A soldier unafraid.

2. My faith is like a staff of oak,
   O let me on it lean!
   My faith, it is a sharpened sword,
   May falsehood find it keen.
   Now fill me with Your Spirit Lord,
   Teach and change me through Your word,
   And by Your love may I be stirred,
   As all true saints have been.

Thomas Toke Lynch, 1818-1871
Altered © 1986 Horrobin/Leavers

169 My God is so big

arr. Phil Burt

My God is so big, so strong and so migh-ty, There's no-thing that He can-not do.

The ri-vers are His, the moun-tains are His, The stars are His han-di-work too. My

God is so big, so strong and so migh - ty, There's no - thing that He can - not do.____

1. My God is so big, so strong and so mighty, } *repeat*
   There's nothing that He cannot do.
   The rivers are His, the mountains are His,
   The stars are His handiwork too.
   My God is so big, so strong and so mighty,
   There's nothing that He cannot do.

2. My God is so big, so strong and so mighty, } *repeat*
   There's nothing that He cannot do.
   He's called you to live, for Him ev'ry day,
   In all that you say and you do.
   My God is so big, so strong and so mighty,
   He can do all things through you.

170 My Lord is higher than a mountain

Words and music
I. Smale
arr. Phil Burt

My Lord is high-er than a moun-tain, He is strong-er than an ar-my, He is wi-ser than a-ny man can tell. My Lord is fast-er than a roc-ket, Can see more than a te-le-scope, Is big-ger than the u-ni-verse as well. His love is warm-er than the burn-ing sun,

Clo - ser than the near - est friend, More real than a - ny truth can be. My Lord, He knows a - bout the past, And He knows a - bout the fu - ture, And He al - so knows all a - bout me.

My Lord is higher than a mountain,
He is stronger than an army,
He is wiser than any man can tell.
My Lord is faster than a rocket,
Can see more than a telescope,
Is bigger than the universe as well.
His love is warmer than the burning sun,
Closer than the nearest friend,
More real than any truth can be.
My Lord, He knows about the past,
And He knows about the future,
And He also knows all about me.

I. Smale

293

171 New every morning

MELCOMBE 8 8 8 8 (LM)   S. Webbe (1740-1816)

Capo 1

New ev-ery morn-ing is the love

Our wa-king and up-ris-ing prove:

Through sleep and dark-ness saf-ely brought,

Re-stored to life and power and thought.

1. New every morning is the love
   Our waking and uprising prove:
   Through sleep and darkness safely brought,
   Restored to life and power and thought.

2. New mercies, each returning day,
   Surround your people as they pray:
   New dangers past, new sins forgiven,
   New thoughts of God, new hopes of heaven.

3. If in our daily life our mind
   Be set to honour all we find,
   New treasures still, of countless price,
   God will provide for sacrifice.

4. The trivial round, the common task,
   Will give us all we ought to ask:
   Room to deny ourselves, a road
   To bring us daily nearer God.

5. Prepare us, Lord, in Your dear love
   For perfect rest with You above,
   And help us, this and every day,
   To grow more like You as we pray.

J. Keble, 1792-1866

172 Now be strong

Words and music
J. H. Cansdale

Now be strong and ve-ry cou-rage-ous, For I have com-man-ded you.
Be not a-fraid Be not dis-mayed; You will have vic - to - ry.___
I will be with you un - til the end, Cap-tain and Lea-der, Guide and Friend.

Now be strong and very courageous,
For I have commanded you.
Be not afraid
Be not dismayed;
You will have victory.
I will be with you until the end,
Captain and Leader,
Guide and Friend.

Altered 1986 Horrobin/Leavers

173 Now the day is over

EUDOXIA 65.65

S. Baring-Gould (1834-1924)

1. Now the day is over,
   Night will soon be here,
   Help me to remember
   You are always near.

2. As the darkness gathers,
   Stars shine overhead,
   Creatures, birds and flowers
   Rest their weary heads.

3. Father, give all people
   Calm and peaceful rest,
   Through Your gracious presence
   May our sleep be blessed.

4. Comfort every sufferer
   Watching late in pain;
   Those who plan some evil
   From their sin restrain.

5. When the morning wakes me,
   Ready for the day,
   Help me, Lord, to serve you,
   Walking in your way.

6. Glory to the Father,
   Glory to the Son;
   And to the Holy Spirit
   Blessing everyone.

S. Baring-Gould
Altered © 1986 Horrobin/Leavers

297

174 Now the green blade
(Love is come again)

NOËL NOUVELET

Capo 3

French melody
arr. Martin Shaw (1875-1958)

Now the green blade ris-eth from the bu-ried grain,

Wheat that in the dark earth ma-ny days has lain.

Love lives a-gain, that with the dead has been;

Love is come a-gain, like wheat that spring-eth green.

1. Now the green blade riseth from the buried grain,
   Wheat that in the dark earth many days has lain.
   Love lives again, that with the dead has been;
   Love is come again, like wheat that springeth green.

2. In the grave they laid him, Love whom men had slain,
   Thinking that never He would wake again;
   Laid in the earth like grain that sleeps unseen,
   Love is come again, like wheat that springeth green.

3. Forth he came at Easter, like the risen grain,
   He that for three days in the grave had lain.
   Quick from the dead my risen Lord is seen;
   Love is come again, like wheat that springeth green.

4. When our hearts are wintry, grieving, or in pain,
   Your touch can call us back to life again.
   Fields of our hearts that dead and bare have been;
   Love is come again, like wheat that springeth green.

J.M.C. Crum, 1872-1958

175 Now thank we all our God

NUN DANKET 6.7.6.7.6.6.6.6.
Capo 3

J. Crüger (1598-1662)

Now thank we all our God, With hearts, and hands, and voi - ces; Who won - drous things has done, In whom His world re - joic - es; Who, from our moth - ers' arms, Has blessed us on our way With

count-less gifts of love, And still is ours to - day.

1. Now thank we all our God,
   With hearts, and hands, and voices;
   Who wondrous things has done,
   In whom His world rejoices;
   Who, from our mothers' arms,
   Has blessed us on our way
   With countless gifts of love,
   And still is ours today.

2. We thank You then, O God
   That through our life You're near us.
   For joy that fills our hearts
   Which with Your peace restores us.
   Lord, keep us in Your grace
   And guide us when perplexed,
   That we may love Your ways
   In this world and the next.

3. All praise and thanks to God
   The Father now be given,
   The Son, and Him who reigns
   With Them in highest heaven:
   The one, eternal God,
   Whom earth and heaven adore;
   For thus it was, is now,
   And shall be evermore.

Martin Rinkart, 1586-1649
tr. by Katherine Winkworth, 1829-1878
Altered © 1986 Horrobin/Leavers.

176 O come, all you faithful

Eighteenth century melody probably by
J.F. Wade (1711-1786)
Harmonised mainly by W.H. Monk (1823-1889)

ADESTE FIDELES Irreg.

O Come, all you faith-ful, Joy-ful and tri-um-phant, O come now, O come _ now to Beth - le - hem; Come and be-hold Him, Born the King of an - gels: O come, let us a - dore Him, O come, let us a - dore Him, O

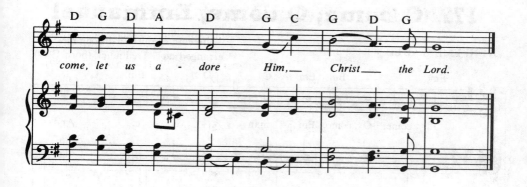

come, let us a - dore Him,— Christ— the Lord.

1. O Come. all you faithful,
   Joyful and triumphant,
   O come now, O come now to Bethlehem;
   Come and behold Him,
   Born the King of angels:

   O come, let us adore Him,
   O come, let us adore Him,
   O come, let us adore Him,
   Christ the Lord.

2. True God of true God,
   Light of light eternal,
   He, who abhors not the virgin's womb;
   Son of the Father,
   Begotten not created:
      O come, let us adore Him . . .

3. Sing like the angels,
   Sing in exultation,
   Sing with the citizens of heaven above,
   'Glory to God,
   Glory in the highest':
      O come, let us adore Him . . .

4. Yes, Lord, we greet You,
   Born that happy morning,
   Jesus, to You be glory given;
   Word of the Father,
   Then in flesh appearing:
      O come, let us adore Him . . .

   Latin, 18th cent.
   tr. Frederick Oakley, 1802-1880
   Altered © 1986 Horrobin/Leavers

177 O come, O come, Emmanuel

VENI EMMANUEL 8 8 8 8 8 8

Fifteenth century Plainsong melody
arranged Noël Tredinnick (born 1949)

O come, O come, Em-man-u-el And ran-som cap-tive Is-ra-el Who mourns in lone-ly ex-ile here Un-til the Son of God____ draws near: Re-joice, re-joice! Em-man-u-

el shall come to you O Is - ra - el.

1. O come, O come, Emmanuel
   And ransom captive Israel
   Who mourns in lonely exile here
   Until the Son of God draws near:
   Rejoice, rejoice!
   Emmanuel shall come to you O Israel.

2. O come, true Branch of Jesse, free
   Your children from this tyranny;
   From depths of hell Your people save,
   To rise victorious from the grave:
       Rejoice, rejoice . . .

3. O come, bright Daybreak, come and cheer
   Our spirits by Your advent here;
   Dispel the long night's lingering gloom
   And pierce the shadows of the tomb:
       Rejoice, rejoice . . .

4. O come, strong Key of David, come
   And open wide our heavenly home;
   Make safe the way that leads on high
   And close the path to misery:
       Rejoice, rejoice . . .

5. O come, O come, great Lord of might
   Who long ago on Sinai's height
   Gave all Your tribes the ancient law
   In cloud and majesty and awe:
       Rejoice, rejoice . . .

> *from the Latin (thirteenth century)*
> *J. M. Neale 1818-1866 and others*
> © in this version *Jubilate Hymns*

178 O happy day!

Ron Jones

Capo 1

O hap-py day __ that fixed my choice On You, my Sav-iour and my God! __ Well may this grate - ful heart re - joice __ And tell of Christ's re - deem - ing blood. *O hap-py day, __ O hap-py day, __ When Je - sus washed my sins a - way, __ He taught me*

how to watch and pray, And live re-joic-ing ev-'ry day; O hap-py

day, — O hap-py day, — When Je-sus washed my sins a - way. —

1. O happy day that fixed my choice
   On You, my Saviour and my God!
   Well may this grateful heart rejoice
   And tell of Christ's redeeming blood.

   O happy day, O happy day,
   When Jesus washed my sins away,
   He taught me how to watch and pray,
   And live rejoicing ev'ry day; (Hallelujah!)
   O happy day, O happy day,
   When Jesus washed my sins away.

2. It's done, the great transaction's done!
   I am my Lord's, and He is mine;
   He led me, and I followed on
   Responding to the voice divine.
      O happy day, . . .

3. Now rest, my long-divided heart,
   In Jesus Christ who loves you, rest
   And never from your Lord depart—
   Enriched in Him, by Him possessed!
      O happy day, . . .

4. So God, who heard my solemn vow,
   In daily prayer shall hear my voice
   Till in my final breath I bow
   And bless the day that fixed my choice.
      O happy day, . . .

P. Doddridge 1702-1751
Altered © 1986 Horrobin/Leavers

307

179 O Lord my God!

HOW GREAT THOU ART
Majestically

Russian hymn tune
arr. Stuart K. Hine (1899–1989)

O Lord my God! when I in awe-some won - der Con - si - der all the works Thy hand hath made, I see the stars, I hear the migh-ty thun - der,___ Thy pow'r through - out the un - i - verse dis - play'd: *Then sings my soul, my Sa-viour God, to Thee,* *How great Thou*

1. O Lord my God! when I in awe-some wonder
   Consider all the works Thy hand hath made,
   I see the stars, I hear the mighty thunder,
   Thy pow'r throughout the universe display'd:

   Then sings my soul, my Saviour God, to Thee,
   How great Thou art! How great Thou art!
   Then sings my soul, my Saviour God, to Thee,
   How great Thou art! How great Thou art!

2. When through the woods and forest glades I wander
   And hear the birds sing sweetly in the trees;
   When I look down from lofty mountain grandeur,
   And hear the brook, and feel the gentle breeze;
   Then sings my soul, . . .

3. And when I think that God His Son not sparing,
   Sent Him to die— I scarce can take it in.
   That on the cross my burden gladly bearing,
   He bled and died to take away my sin:
   Then sings my soul, . . .

4. When Christ shall come with shout of acclamation
   And take me home— what joy shall fill my heart!
   Then shall I bow in humble adoration
   And there proclaim, my God, how great Thou art!
   Then sings my soul, . . .

> *Russian hymn*
> *tr. Stuart K. Hine*
> *© 1953 Kingsway's Thankyou Music*

309

180 Oh! Oh! Oh! how good is the Lord

Anon.
arr. Jeanne Harper

With joyful abandon

Oh! Oh! Oh! how good is the Lord.

Oh! Oh! Oh! how good is the Lord. Oh! Oh! Oh! how

good is the Lord. I ne-ver will for-get what He has done for me.

He gives me sal-va-tion, how good is the Lord. He

Oh! Oh! Oh! how good is the Lord.
Oh! Oh! Oh! how good is the Lord.
Oh! Oh! Oh! how good is the Lord.
I never will forget what He has done for me.

1. He gives me salvation, how good is the Lord.
   He gives me salvation, how good is the Lord.
   He gives me salvation, how good is the Lord.
   I never will forget what He has done for me.
   Oh! Oh! Oh! . . .

2. He gives me His blessings . . .
   Oh! Oh! Oh! . . .

3. He gives me His Spirit . . .
   Oh! Oh! Oh! . . .

4. He gives me His healing . . .
   Oh! Oh! Oh! . . .

5. He gives me His glory . . .
   Oh! Oh! Oh! . . .

Other suitable verses may be added.
He gives us each other . . . His body . . . His freedom, *etc.*

Copyright control

181 Oh, the love that drew

Wm.R. Newell

D. B. Towner (1833–1896)

Oh, the love that drew sal - va - tion's plan! Oh, the grace that brought it down to man! Oh, the migh - ty gulf that God did span at Cal - va - ry! Mer - cy there was great, and grace was free; Par - don there was mul - ti - plied to me;

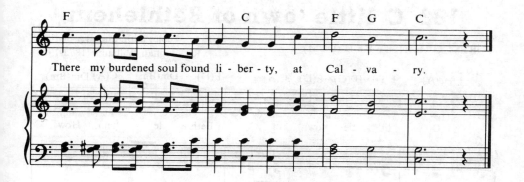

There my burdened soul found li - ber - ty, at Cal - va - ry.

Oh, the love that drew salvation's plan!
Oh, the grace that brought it down to man!
Oh, the mighty gulf that God did span at Calvary!
Mercy there was great, and grace was free;
Pardon there was multiplied to me;
There my burdened soul found liberty, at Calvary.

W. R. Newell, 1868–1956
Copyright control

182 O little town of Bethlehem

FOREST GREEN 8 6 8 6 D (DCM)

coll., adpt. and arr. by
R. Vaughan Williams (1872-1958)

Capo 3

e - ver - last - ing   Light;   The   hopes and fears of

all   the   years   Are   met   in   you   to - night.

1. O little town of Bethlehem,
   How still we see you lie!
   Above your deep and dreamless sleep
   The silent stars go by:
   Yet in your dark streets shining
   Is everlasting Light;
   The hopes and fears of all the years
   Are met in you tonight.

2. For Christ is born of Mary;
   And, gathered all above
   While mortals sleep, the angels keep
   Their watch of wondering love.
   O morning stars, together
   Proclaim the holy birth,
   And praises sing to God the King,
   And peace to men on earth.

3. How silently, how silently,
   The wondrous gift is given!
   So God imparts to human hearts
   The blessings of His heaven.
   No ear may hear His coming;
   But in this world of sin,
   Where meek souls will receive Him, still
   The dear Christ enters in.

4. O holy child of Bethlehem,
   Descend to us, we pray;
   Cast out our sin, and enter in;
   Be born in us today.
   We hear the Christmas angels
   The great glad tidings tell;
   O come to us, abide with us,
   Our Lord Immanuel.

Phillips Brooks, 1835-1893

183 On Calvary's tree

A.W. Edsor

Melody: A.E. Walton
arr. Norman Warren

On Calvary's tree He died for me,
That I His love might know;
To set me free He died for me
That's why I love Him so.

A.W. Edsor

184 Oh, the Lord looked down

Words and melody
Traditional

Oh, the Lord looked down from his win-dow in the sky, Said: 'I cre-a-ted man, but I can't re-mem-ber why! Noth-ing but fight-ing since cre-a-tion day. I'll send a lit-tle wa-ter and wash them all a-way.' Oh, the Lord came down and looked a-round a spell. There was Mis-ter Noah be-

having mighty well. And that is the reason the Scriptures record

No-ah found grace in the eyes of the Lord. Noah found grace in the

eyes of the Lord, Noah found grace in the eyes of the Lord,

Noah found grace in the eyes of the Lord, And he left him high and dry.

1. Oh, the Lord looked down from his window in the sky,
   Said: 'I created man, but I can't remember why!
   Nothing but fighting since creation day.
   I'll send a little water and wash them all away.'
   Oh, the Lord came down and looked around a spell.
   There was Mr Noah behaving mighty well.
   And that is the reason the Scriptures record
   Noah found grace in the eyes of the Lord.

   Noah found grace in the eyes of the Lord,
   Noah found grace in the eyes of the Lord,
   Noah found grace in the eyes of the Lord,
   And he left him high and dry.

2. The Lord said: 'Noah, there's going to be a flood,
   There's going to be some water, there's going to be some mud,
   So, take off your hat, Noah, take off your coat,
   Get Shem, Ham and Japheth and build yourself a boat.'
   Noah said: 'Lord, I don't believe I could.'
   The Lord said: 'Noah, get yourself some wood.
   You never know what you can do till you try.
   Build it fifty cubits wide and thirty cubits high.'
      Noah found grace in the eyes of the Lord . . .

3. Noah said: 'There she is, there she is, Lord!'
   The Lord said: 'Noah, it's time to get aboard.
   Take of each creature a he and a she,
   And of course take Mrs Noah and the whole family.'
   Noah said: 'Lord, it's getting mighty dark.'
   The Lord said: 'Noah, get those creatures in the ark.'
   Noah said: 'Lord, it's beginning to pour.'
   The Lord said: 'Noah, hurry up and close the door.'
      Noah found grace . . .

4. The ark rose up on the bosom of the deep.
   After forty days Mr Noah took a peep.
   He said: 'We're not moving, Lord, where are we at?'
   The Lord said: 'You're sitting right on Mount Ararat.'
   Noah said: 'Lord, it's getting nice and dry.'
   The Lord said: 'Noah, see my rainbow in the sky.
   Take all your creatures and people the earth,
   And be sure that you're not more trouble than you're worth.'
      Noah found grace . . .

185 Once, in royal David's city

IRBY 8 7. 8 7. 7 7

Capo 3

Henry John Gauntlett (1805-1876)

1. Once in royal David's city,
   Stood a lowly cattle shed,
   Where a mother laid her Baby,
   In a manger for His bed.
   Mary was that mother mild,
   Jesus Christ her little child.

2. He came down to earth from heaven,
   Who is God and Lord of all,
   And His shelter was a stable,
   And His cradle was a stall:
   With the poor and mean and lowly
   Lived on earth our Saviour holy.

3. And through all his wondrous childhood
   He would honour and obey,
   Love and watch the lowly mother,
   In whose gentle arms He lay.
   Christian children all should be,
   Kind, obedient, good as He.

4. For He is our childhood's pattern:
   Day by day like us He grew;
   He was little, weak, and helpless;
   Tears and smiles like us He knew:
   And He feels for all our sadness,
   And He shares in all our gladness.

5. And our eyes at last shall see Him
   Through His own redeeming love;
   For that Child, so dear and gentle,
   Is our Lord in heaven above;
   And He leads His children on
   To the place where He is gone.

6. Not in that poor, lowly stable,
   With the oxen standing by,
   We shall see Him, but in heaven,
   Set at God's right hand on high;
   There His children gather round
   Bright like stars, with glory crowned.

Cecil Frances Alexander, 1823-1895

186 On Jordan's bank

WINCHESTER NEW L.M.

From a chorale in the *Musicalisch Handbuch*,
Hamburg, 1690, arr. W.H. Havergal, (1793-1870)

Capo 1

1. On Jordan's bank the Baptist's cry
   Announces that the Lord is nigh;
   Come then and listen for he brings
   Glad tidings from the King of kings.

2. Then cleansed be every heart from sin;
   Make straight the way for God within;
   Prepare we in our hearts a home,
   Where such a mighty guest may come.

3. For You are our salvation, Lord,
   Our refuge and our great reward;
   Without Your grace we waste away,
   Like flowers that wither and decay.

4. To Him who left the throne of heaven
   To save mankind, all praise be given;
   To God the Father, voices raise,
   And Holy Spirit, let us praise.

Charles Coffin, 1676-1749,
tr. John Chandler, 1806-1876, altd.
Altered © 1986 Horrobin/Leavers

187 One day when heaven

C. H. Marsh (1886–1956)

One day when hea-ven was filled with His prais-es, One day when sin was as black as could be,_____ Je-sus came down to be born of a vir-gin, Lived a-mong men, my ex-am-ple is

1. One day when heaven was filled with His praises,
   One day when sin was as black as could be,
   Jesus came down to be born of a virgin,
   Lived among men, my example is He!

   Living, He lov'd me; dying, He saved me;
   Buried, He carried my sins far away,
   Rising, He justified freely for ever:
   One day He's coming O glorious day.

2. One day they led Him up Calvary's mountain,
   One day they nailed Him to die on the tree;
   Suffering anguish, despis'd and rejected;
   Bearing our sins, my Redeemer is He!
   Living, He lov'd me . . .

3. One day they left Him alone in the garden,
   One day He rested, from suffering free;
   Angels came down o'er His tomb to keep vigil;
   Hope of the hopeless my Saviour is He!
   Living, He lov'd me . . .

4. One day the grave could conceal Him no longer,
   One day the stone rolled away from the door;
   Then He arose, over death He had conquer'd;
   Now is ascended, my Lord evermore!
   Living, He lov'd me . . .

5. One day the trumpet will sound for His coming,
   One day the skies with His glory will shine;
   Wonderful day my beloved ones bringing;
   Glorious Saviour, this Jesus is mine!
   Living, He lov'd me . . .

J. Wilbur Chapman, 1859–1918

188 One more step along the world I go

Words and music
Sydney Carter
arr Douglas Coombes

With a spring

One more step a-long the world I go, One more step a-long the world I go, From the old things to the new

Keep me tra-vel-ling a-long with You. *And it's from the old I*

trav-el to the new, Keep me tra-vel-ling a-long with You.

1. One more step along the world I go,
   One more step along the world I go,
   From the old things to the new
   Keep me travelling along with You.

   And it's from the old I travel to the new,
   Keep me travelling along with You.

2. Round the corners of the world I turn,
   More and more about the world I learn.
   And the new things that I see
   You'll be looking at along with me.
   And it's from the old . . .

3. As I travel through the bad and good
   Keep me travelling the way I should.
   Where I see no way to go
   You'll be telling me the way, I know.
   And it's from the old . . .

4. Give me courage when the world is rough,
   Keep me loving though the world is tough.
   Leap and sing in all I do,
   Keep me travelling along with You.
   And it's from the old . . .

5. You are older than the world can be
   You are younger than the life in me.
   Ever old and ever new,
   Keep me travelling along with You.
   And its from the old . . .

Sydney Carter, b. 1915

189 One, two, three, Jesus loves me

Lisa Mazak

Happily

One, two, three, Je-sus loves me. One, two, Je-sus loves you 1. Three, four, He loves you more Than you've ev-er been loved be-fore. 2. Five, six, seven, we're go-ing to heav'n. Eight, nine, it's tru-ly di-vine.

One, two, three, Jesus loves me.
One, two, Jesus loves you

1. Three, four, He loves you more
   Than you've ever been loved before.
      One, two, three, . . .

2. Five, six, seven, we're going to heav'n.
   Eight, nine, it's truly divine.
      One, two, three, . . .

3. Nine, ten, its time to end;
   But instead we'll sing it again
   (There's no time to sing it again).
      One, two, three, . . .

190 Only a boy called David

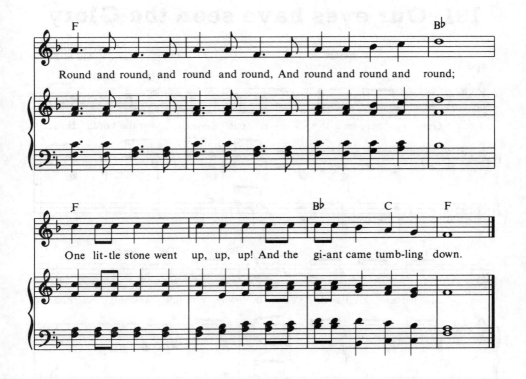

Round and round, and round and round, And round and round and round;

One lit-tle stone went up, up, up! And the gi-ant came tumb-ling down.

Only a boy called David,
Only a rippling brook;
Only a boy called David,
Five little stones he took.
Then, one little stone went in the sling,
And the sling went round and round,
One little stone went in the sling,
And the sling went round and round,
Round and round, and round and round,
And round and round and round;
One little stone went up, up, up!
And the giant came tumbling down.

191 Our eyes have seen the Glory

Music: Traditional
arr. Robin Sheldon

Capo 3

Our eyes have seen the glo - ry of our Sa-viour, Christ the Lord; He's

sea - ted at his Fa - ther's side in love and full ac-cord; From

there up-on the sons of men his Spi-rit is out-poured, All hail, as - cend - ed

King! *Glo - ry, glo-ry, hal - le - lu - jah,*

1. Our eyes have seen the glory of our Saviour, Christ the Lord;
   He's seated at His Father's side in love and full accord;
   From there upon the sons of men His Spirit is outpoured,
   All hail, ascended King!

   Glory, glory, hallelujah,
   Glory, glory, hallelujah,
   Glory, glory, hallelujah,
   All hail, ascended King!

2. He came to earth at Christmas and was made a man like us;
   He taught, He Healed, He suffered— and they nailed Him to the cross;
   He rose again on Easter Day— our Lord victorious,
   All hail, ascended King!
      Glory, glory, . . .

3. The good news of His kingdom must be preached to every shore,
   The news of peace and pardon, and the end of strife and war;
   The secret of His kingdom is to serve Him evermore,
   All hail, ascended King!
      Glory, glory, . . .

4. His kingdom is a family of men of every race,
   They live their lives in harmony, enabled by His grace;
   They follow His example till they see Him face to face,
   All hail, ascended King!
      Glory, glory, . . .

© *Roland Meredith.*

192 Our Father who is in heaven

CARIBBEAN LORD'S PRAYER

arr. Allen Percival

1. Our Father who is in heaven,
   Hallowed be Your Name,
   Your Kingdom come, Your will be done,
   Hallowed be Your Name.

2. On earth as it is in heaven,
   Hallowed be Your Name,
   Give us this day our daily bread,
   Hallowed be Your Name.

3. Forgive us all our trespasses,
   Hallowed be Your Name,
   As we forgive those who trespass against us,
   Hallowed be Your Name.

4. And lead us not into temptation,
   Hallowed be Your Name,
   But deliver us from all that is evil,
   Hallowed be Your Name.

5. For Yours is the Kingdom, the Power
   and the Glory,
   Hallowed be Your Name,
   For ever and for ever and ever
   Hallowed be Your Name.

6. Amen, Amen, it shall be so,
   Hallowed be Your Name,
   Amen, Amen, it shall be so,
   Hallowed be Your Name.

193 Our harvest day is over

Music by Roger Jones

Our har - vest day is ov - er for yet an - oth - er year. The gifts we've brought to Je - sus are now be - fore us here. Be -

(after 3rd verse)

fore we go, a - gain we raise our thanks to God a -
bove For all that He pro - vides us with from
His great hand of love. All
praise to God a - bove!

1. Our harvest day is over for yet another year.
   The gifts we've brought to Jesus are now before us here.
   Before we go, again we raise our thanks to God above
   For all that He provides us with from His great hand of love.

2. We thank God for providing fresh air for us to breathe.
   Thirst-quenching water, also, to us He does bequeath.
   Fresh fruit and daily bread as well are gifts from God above,
   Tinned foods, and eggs, and poultry come from our great God of love.

3. Our clothes and health come also from God's all-gracious hand;
   Our happiness is something which He again has planned.
   But something more important still comes to us through God's love—
   Eternal life through His dear Son; all praise to God above!
       All praise to God above!

194 O sinner man

Words and music
Spiritual

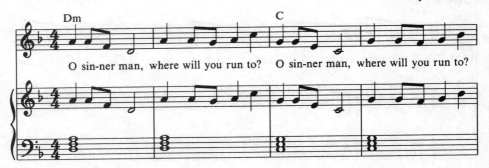

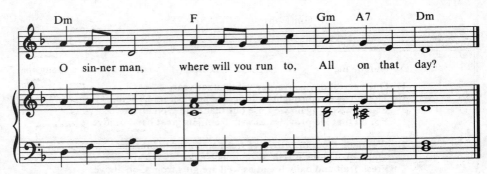

O sinner man, where will you run to?
O sinner man, where will you run to?
O sinner man, where will you run to,
All on that day?

1. Run to the rocks, rocks won't you hide me?
   Run to the rocks, rocks won't you hide me?
   Run to the rocks, rocks won't you hide me,
   All on that day?
      O sinner man . . .

2. Run to the sea, sea is a-boiling,
   Run to the sea, sea is a-boiling,
   Run to the sea, sea is a-boiling,
   All on that day.
      O sinner man . . .

3. Run to the Lord, Lord won't you hide me?
   Run to the Lord, Lord won't you hide me?
   Run to the Lord, Lord won't you hide me,
   All on that day?
      O sinner man . . .

4. O sinner man, should bin a-praying
   O sinner man, should bin a-praying
   O sinner man, should bin a-praying
   All on that day.
      O sinner man . . .

Copyright control

195 O when the saints go marching in

Traditional
arr. David Wilson

Capo 1

F(E)

O when the saints_____ go march-ing in, _____O when the
(O when the saints)   (go march-ing in)

Gm(F#m)   C7(A7)   F(E)   F7(E7)

saints go march-ing in;_____ O Lord, I want to be a-mong the

Bb(A)   Gm(F#m)   F(E) Bb(A) F(E) Bb(A) F(E)

num-ber_____ When the saints go march-ing in!_____

Arrangement Copyright © David Wilson / Jubilate Hymns
Used by permission

1. O when the saints go marching in,
   O when the saints go marching in;
   O Lord, I want to be among the number
   When the saints go marching in!

2. O when they crown Him Lord of all,
   O when they crown Him Lord of all;
   O Lord, I want to be among the number
   When they crown Him Lord of all.

3. O when all knees bow at His name,
   O when all knees bow at His name,
   O Lord, I want to be among the number
   When all knees bow at His name.

4. O when they sing the Saviour's praise,
   O when they sing the Saviour's praise,
   O Lord, I want to be among the number
   When they sing the Saviour's praise.

5. O when the saints go marching in,
   O when the saints go marching in;
   O Lord, I want to be among the number
   When the saints go marching in!

196 Peace I give to you

Jn 14:27;2 Cor 1:3-4

Graham Kendrick

Peace, I give to you, I give to you my peace.

peace. Let it flow to one a - no - ther, let it

flow, let it flow. Let it flow.

1. Peace, I give to you, I give to you my peace.
   Peace, I give to you, I give to you my peace.

   Let it flow to one another, let it flow, let it flow.
   Let it flow to one another, let it flow, let it flow.

2. Love I give to you, I give you my love.
   Love I give to you, I give you my love.
   Let it flow . . .

3. Hope I give to you, I give you my hope.
   Hope I give to you, I give you my hope.
   Let it flow . . .

4. Joy I give to you, I give you my joy.
   Joy I give to you, I give you my joy.
   Let it flow . . .

197 Peter and James and John

arr. Phil Burt

1. Peter and James and John in a sailboat, *(3 times)*
Out on the beautiful sea.

2. They fished all night but they caught nothing, *(3 times)*
Out on the beautiful sea.

3. Along came Jesus walking on the water, *(3 times)*
Out on the beautiful sea.

4. He said 'Throw your nets over on the other side', *(3 times)*
Out on the beautiful sea.

5. The nets were filled with great big fishes, *(3 times)*
Out on the beautiful sea.

6. The lesson of this story is listen to the Lord, *(3 times)*
Wherever you may be.

198 Peter and John went to pray
(Silver and Gold)

Anon.
arr. Betty Pulkingham

Pe - ter and John went to pray, ___ They met a lame man on the way. He asked for alms ___ and held out his palms, And this is what Pe - ter did say: ___ 'Sil - ver and Gold have I none, ___ But such as I have I give you, In the

Arrangement © 1974, 1975 Celebration. Administered
in Europe by Kingsway's Thankyou Music, P O Box 75, Eastbourne,
East Sussex, BN23 6NW

name of Je - sus Christ ___ of Naz - areth, Rise up and
walk!' ___ He went walk - ing and leap - ing and prais - ing God.
Walk - ing and leap - ing and prais - ing God. 'In the name of Je - sus
Christ ___ of Naz - a - reth, Rise up and walk.' ___

Peter and John went to pray,
They met a lame man on the way.
He asked for alms and held out his palms,
And this is what Peter did say:

'Silver and Gold have I none,
But such as I have I give you,
In the name of Jesus Christ of Nazareth,
Rise up and walk!'

He went walking and leaping and praising God,
Walking and leaping and praising God.
'In the name of Jesus Christ of Nazareth,
Rise up and walk.'

343

199 Praise God

DOXOLOGY
Thomas Ken

Jimmy Owens

Praise God from whom all blessings flow;
Praise Him all creatures here below.
Praise Him above you heavenly hosts;
Praise Father, Son, and Holy Ghost.

200 Praise Him on the trumpet

J. Kennett

With pace and swing

Praise Him on the trum - pet, the psal - tery and harp

Praise Him on the tim - brel and the dance, Praise Him

with stringed in - stru-ments too.

Praise Him on the loud cym - bals, Praise Him on the loud

cym - bals,_____ Let ev' - ry - thing that has breath praise the

Lord.   Hal - le - lu -jah,   praise the Lord,

Hal - le - lu - jah, praise the Lord,_____ Let ev' - ry - thing that has

breath praise the Lord._____   Hal - le - lu -jah,

Praise Him on the trumpet, the psaltery and harp
Praise Him on the timbrel and the dance,
Praise Him with stringed instruments too.
Praise Him on the loud cymbals
Praise Him on the loud cymbals
Let ev'rything that has breath praise the Lord.
Hallelujah, praise the Lord,
Hallelujah, praise the Lord,
Let ev'rything that has breath praise the Lord.

201 Praise Him, praise Him, all you little children

HE IS LOVE 10 6 10 6

E. Rawdon Bailey (1859–1938)

1. Praise Him, praise Him, all you little children,
   God is love, God is love.
   Praise Him, praise Him, all you little children,
   God is love, God is love.

2. Love Him, love Him, all you little children,
   God is love, God is love.
   Love Him, love Him, all you little children,
   God is love, God is love.

3. Thank Him, thank Him, all you little children,
   God is love, God is love.
   Thank Him, thank Him, all you little children,
   God is love, God is love.

Anon, c. 1890

202 Praise Him, praise Him, praise Him in the morning

arr. Phil Burt

1. Praise Him, praise Him,
   Praise Him in the morning,
   Praise Him in the noontime,
   Praise Him, praise Him,
   Praise Him as the sun goes down.

2. Thank Him . . . *etc.*

3. Love Him . . . *etc.*

4. Serve Him . . . *etc.*

203 Praise Him! Praise Him! Jesus, our blessèd Redeemer

12.10.12.10.11.10.12.10

C.G. Allen (1838-1878)

Capo 1

Praise Him! praise Him! Je - sus, our bless-èd Re - deem - er!

Sing, O earth - His won-der-ful love pro - claim!___

Hail Him! hail Him! high-est arch-ang-els in glo - ry;

Strength and hon - our give to His ho - ly name!___

Fine

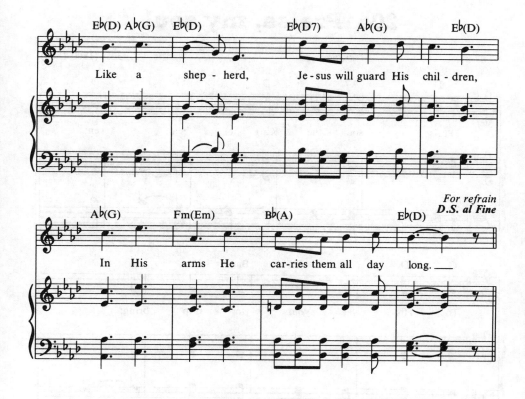

Like a shep-herd, Je-sus will guard His chil-dren,

In His arms He car-ries them all day long. ___

1. Praise Him! praise Him! Jesus, our blessèd Redeemer!
   Sing, O earth — His wonderful love proclaim!
   Hail Him! hail Him! highest archangels in glory;
   Strength and honour give to His holy name!
   Like a shepherd, Jesus will guard His children,
   In His arms He carries them all day long.

   Praise Him! praise Him! tell of His excellent greatness;
   Praise Him! praise Him ever in joyful song!

2. Praise Him! praise Him! Jesus, our blessèd Redeemer!
   For our sins He suffered, and bled, and died;
   He — our rock, our hope of eternal salvation,
   Hail Him! hail Him! Jesus, the crucified!
   Sound His praises — Jesus who bore our sorrows,
   Love unbounded, wonderful, deep and strong.
      Praise Him! praise Him! . . .

3. Praise Him! praise Him! Jesus, our blessèd Redeemer!
   All in heaven let their hosannas ring!
   Jesus, Saviour, reigning for ever and ever:
   Crown Him! crown Him! prophet, and priest, and king!
   Christ is coming, over the world victorious,
   Power and glory unto the Lord belong.
      Praise Him! praise Him! . . .

Frances van Alstyne, 1820-1915
Altered © 1986 Horrobin/Leavers

204 Praise, my soul

87.87.87.   J. Goss (1800-1880)

Praise, my soul, the King of hea - ven;
To His feet your wor - ship bring;
Ran - somed, healed, re - stored, for - gi - ven,
We do now His prais - es sing.

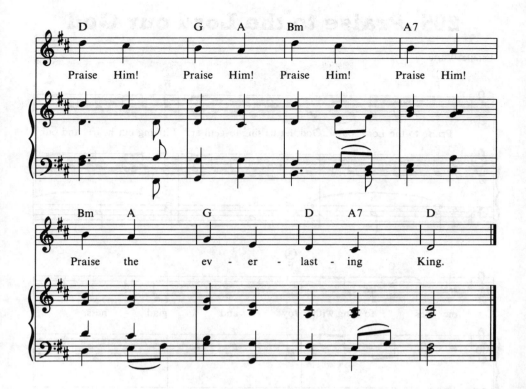

Praise Him! Praise Him! Praise Him! Praise Him!
Praise the ev - er - last - ing King.

1. Praise, my soul, the King of heaven;
   To His feet your worship bring;
   Ransomed, healed, restored, forgiven,
   We do now His praises sing.
   Praise Him! Praise Him! Praise Him! Praise Him!
   Praise the everlasting King.

2. Praise Him for His grace and favour
   To our fathers in distress;
   Praise Him, still the same for ever,
   Merciful, He waits to bless.
   Praise Him! Praise Him! Praise Him! Praise Him!
   Glorious in His faithfulness.

3. Father-like He loves and spares us;
   Well our weaknesses He knows;
   In His hands He gently bears us,
   Rescues us from all our foes;
   Praise Him! Praise Him! Praise Him! Praise Him!
   Widely as His mercy flows.

4. Angels, help us to adore Him!
   You behold Him face to face;
   Sun and moon, bow down before Him;
   Dwellers all in time and space.
   Praise Him! Praise Him! Praise Him! Praise Him!
   Praise with us the God of grace.

H.F. Lyte, 1793-1847
Altered © 1986 Horrobin/Leavers

205 Praise to the Lord our God

Estelle White
Anon

Praise to the Lord our God, let us sing to-geth-er, Lift-ing our hearts and our voic-es to sing with Joy and glad-ness.

Come a-long, a-long, a-long, and sing with praise.

Praise to the Lord our God, let us sing together,
Lifting our hearts and our voices to sing with
Joy and gladness.
Come along, along, along, and sing with praise.

Estelle White

This song can be sung straight through with the accompaniment
or it can be sung unaccompanied as a four-part round.
The circled figures over the music show where each part starts the tune.

206 Put your hand in the hand

Words and music
Gene MacLellan

Put your hand in the hand of the man who stilled the wa-ter. Put your hand in the hand of the man who calmed the sea. Take a look at your-self and you can look at o-thers dif-f'rent-ly, By put-tin' your hand in the hand of the

man from Ga - li - lee.

Ev - 'ry - time I look in - to the Ho - ly Book I want to

trem - ble. When I read a-bout the part where a car-pen-ter cleared the

tem - ple. For the buy-ers and the sel-lers were

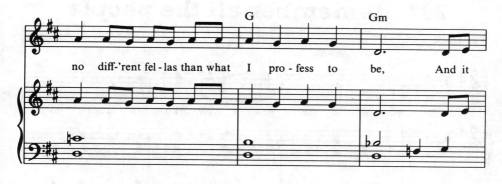

no diff-'rent fel-las than what I pro-fess to be, And it

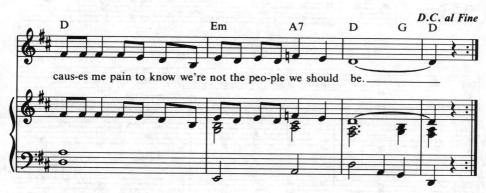

D.C. al Fine

caus-es me pain to know we're not the peo-ple we should be.

1. Put your hand in the hand of the man who stilled the water.
   Put your hand in the hand of the man who calmed the sea.
   Take a look at yourself and you can look at others diff'rently,
   By puttin' your hand in the hand of the man from Galilee.

2. Ev'rytime I look into the Holy Book I want to tremble.
   When I read about the part where a carpenter cleared the temple.
   For the buyers and the sellers were no diff'rent fellas than what I profess to be,
   And it causes me pain to know we're not the people we should be.

3. Put your hand in the hand of the man who stilled the water.
   Put your hand in the hand of the man who calmed the sea.
   Take a look at yourself and you can look at others diff'rently,
   By puttin' your hand in the hand of the man from Galilee.

Gene MacLellan

207 Remember all the people

TYROLESE 76.76.D.

Tyrolese Carol

Re - mem - ber all the peo - ple Who live in far off lands, In strange and love - ly ci - ties, Or roam the des - ert sands, Or farm the moun - tain pas - tures, Or till the end - less plains Where

Words and music from *The BBC Hymnbook*, 1951, by permission of Oxford University Press

chil-dren wade through rice____ fields And watch the cam - el trains:

1. Remember all the people
   Who live in far off lands,
   In strange and lovely cities,
   Or roam the desert sands,
   Or farm the mountain pastures,
   Or till the endless plains
   Where children wade through rice fields
   And watch the camel trains:

2. Some work in sultry forests
   Where apes swing to and fro,
   Some fish in mighty rivers,
   Some hunt across the snow.
   Remember all God's children
   Who yet have never heard
   The truth that comes from Jesus,
   The glory of His Word.

3. God bless the men and women
   Who serve Him oversea;
   God raise up more to help them
   To set the nations free,
   Till all the distant people
   In every foreign place
   Shall understand His Kingdom
   And come into His grace.

   P. Dearmer, 1867-1936

208 Rejoice in the Lord always

A round in 4 parts

Evelyn Tarner

Rejoice in the Lord always, and again I say rejoice!
Rejoice in the Lord always, and again I say rejoice!
Rejoice, rejoice, and again I say rejoice!
Rejoice, rejoice, and again I say rejoice!

Text from *Phil. 4:4*

209 Ride on, ride on

WINCHESTER NEW 8 8 8 8 (LM)

Musikalishes Handbuch Hamburg 1690

Capo 1

Ride on, ride on in ma-jes-ty As all the crowds 'Ho-san-na!' cry: Through wa-ving branch-es slow-ly ride, O Sav-iour, to be cru-ci-fied.

1. Ride on, ride on in majesty
   As all the crowds 'Hosanna!' cry:
   Through waving branches slowly ride,
   O Saviour, to be crucified.

2. Ride on, ride on in majesty,
   In lowly pomp ride on to die:
   O Christ, your triumph now begin
   With captured death, and conquered sin!

3. Ride on, ride on in majesty—
   The angel armies of the sky
   Look down with sad and wondering eyes
   To see the approaching sacrifice.

4. Ride on, ride on in majesty,
   The last and fiercest foe defy:
   The Father on his sapphire throne
   Awaits his own anointed Son.

5. Ride on, ride on in majesty,
   In lowly pomp ride on to die:
   Bow your meek head to mortal pain,
   Then take, O God, your power and reign!

H. Milman 1791-1868
© *in this version* Jubilate Hymns

361

210 Rise and shine
(Arky, arky song)

Words and music:
Traditional
arr. E. J. Hume

Rise, and shine, and give God his glory, glory.
Rise, and shine, and give God his glory, glory.
Rise, and shine, and give God his glory, glory,
children of the Lord.

1. The Lord said to Noah: 'There's gonna be a floody, floody.'
   Lord said to Noah: 'There's gonna be a floody, floody.
   Get those children out of the muddy, muddy,
   children of the Lord.'
        Rise, and shine, . . .

2. The Lord told Noah to build him an arky, arky,
   The Lord told Noah to build him an arky, arky,
   Build it out of gopher barky, barky,
   children of the Lord.
        Rise, and shine, . . .

3. The animals, the animals, they came on, by twosies, twosies,
   The animals, the animals, they came on, by twosies, twosies,
   Elephants and kangaroosies, 'roosies,
   children of the Lord.
        Rise, and shine, . . .

4. It rained and poured for forty daysies, daysies,
   It rained and poured for forty daysies, daysies,
   Almost drove those animals crazies, crazies,
   children of the Lord.
        Rise, and shine, . . .

5. The sun came out and dried up the landy, landy
   The sun came out and dried up the landy, landy
   Everything was fine and dandy, dandy,
   children of the Lord.
        Rise, and shine, . . .

211 Said Judas to Mary

JUDAS AND MARY

Words and music
Sydney Carter (b. 1915)

1. Said Judas to Mary, 'Now what will you do
   With your ointment so rich and so rare?'
   I'll pour it all over the feet of the Lord
   And I'll wipe it away with my hair,' she said.
   I'll wipe it away with my hair.'

2. 'Oh Mary, oh Mary, oh think of the poor—
   This ointment it could have been sold;
   And think of the blankets and think of the bread
   You could buy with the silver and gold,' he said,
   You could buy with the silver and gold.'

3. 'Tomorrow, tomorrow I'll think of the poor,
   Tomorrow,' she said, 'not today;
   For dearer than all of the poor of the world
   Is my love who is going away,' she said,
   My love who is going away.'

4. Said Jesus to Mary, 'Your love is so deep,
   Today you may do as you will;
   Tomorrow, you say, I am going away,
   But my body I leave with you still,' he said,
   'My body I leave with you still.'

5. 'The poor of the world are my body,' he said,
   'To the end of the world they shall be;
   The bread and the blankets you give to the poor
   You'll find you have given to me,' he said,
   'You'll find you have given to me.'

6. 'My body will hang on the cross of the world
   Tomorrow,' he said, 'and today,
   And Martha and Mary will find me again
   And wash all my sorrow away,' he said,
   'And wash all my sorrow away.'

Sydney Carter, b. 1915

212 Search me, O God

M. Kaihau

C. Scott

Search me, O God, and know my heart today;
Try me, O Lord, and know my thoughts I pray:
See if there be some wicked way in me,
Cleanse me from ev'ry sin and set me free.

M. Kaihau

213 See, amid the winter snow

HUMILITY 7 7 7 7 and chorus

J. Goss (1800-1880)

See, a-mid the win - ter snow, Born for us on earth be-low;

See, the Son of God ap-pears, Pro-mised from e - ter - nal years:

Hail, O ev - er - bless-èd morn! Hail, re-demp-tion's hap - py dawn!

Sing through all Je - ru - sa-lem: 'Christ is born in Beth - le-hem!'

1. See, amid the winter snow,
   Born for us on earth below;
   See, the Son of God appears,
   Promised from eternal years:

   Hail, O ever-blessèd morn!
   Hail, redemption's happy dawn!
   Sing through all Jerusalem:
   'Christ is born in Bethlehem!'

2. Low within a manger lies
   He who built the starry skies;
   He who, throned in heaven's height,
   Reigns in power and glorious light:
      Hail, O ever-blessèd morn . . .

3. Say, you humble shepherds, say
   What's your joyful news today?
   Tell us why you left your sheep
   On the lonely mountain steep:
      Hail, O ever-blessèd morn . . .

4. 'As we watched at dead of night,
   All around us shone a light;
   Angels, singing peace on earth,
   Told us of a Saviour's birth.'
      Hail, O ever-blessèd morn . . .

5. Sacred baby, king most dear,
   What a tender love was here,
   Down He came from glory high
   In a manger there to lie.
      Hail, O ever-blessèd morn . . .

6. Holy Saviour, born on earth,
   Teach us by Your lowly birth;
   Grant that we may ever be
   Taught by such humility.
      Hail, O ever-blessèd morn . . .

E Caswall, 1814–1875
Altered © 1986 Horrobin/Leavers

214 See Him lying on a bed of straw

CALYPSO CAROL Irregular

Michael Perry (b. 1942)
arr. Stephen Coates (b. 1952)

See Him ly - ing on a bed of straw: draughty sta - ble with an op - en door; Ma - ry cra - dl-ing the babe she bore The Prince of glo - ry is His name.

O now car - ry me to Beth - le - hem ___ To

1. See Him lying on a bed of straw:
   A draughty stable with an open door;
   Mary cradling the babe she bore—
   The Prince of glory is His name.

   O now carry me to Bethlehem
   To see the Lord appear to men!
   Just as poor as was the stable then,
   The Prince of glory when He came.

2. Star of silver, sweep across the skies,
   Show where Jesus in the manger lies;
   Shepherds swiftly from your stupor rise
   To see the Saviour of the world!
     O now carry . . .

3. Angels, sing the song that you began,
   Bring God's glory to the heart of man;
   Sing that Bethl'em's little baby can
   Be salvation to the soul.
     O now carry . . .

4. Mine are riches, from Your poverty,
   From Your innocence, eternity;
   Mine forgiveness by Your death for me,
   Child of sorrow for my joy.
     O now carry . . .

© *Michael Perry*

215 Seek ye first

Karen Lafferty
arr. Roland Fudge

ness, And all these things shall be add-ed un-to you.

lu - ia. *al - le - lu - ia.*

Al - le - lu, al - le - lu - ia.

(Sing each verse two times. For the repeat half of the group should sing the *Alleluia* descant as written)

1. Seek ye first the Kingdom of God,
   And his righteousness,
   And all these things shall be added unto you.
   Allelu, alleluia.

2. Man shall not live by bread alone,
   But by every word,
   That proceeds from the mouth of God.
   Allelu, alleluia.

3. Ask and it shall be given unto you,
   Seek and you shall find,
   Knock and the door shall be opened up to you.
   Allelu, alleluia.

216 Saviour of the world

Words and music
Greg Leavers
arr. Phil Burt

*Begin slowly — with increasing
excitement in verses 2 & 3*

Capo 3

Sa-viour of the world, thank you for dy-ing on the cross. All

praise to You our ris-en Lord, Hal-le-lu-jah! Je-sus.

In the gar-den of Geth-se-ma-ne Je-sus knelt and prayed, __

For He knew the time was near when He would be be-trayed. __

374

God gave Him the strength to cope with all that peo-ple
did to hurt Him; Sol-diers laughed and forced a crown of
thorns u-pon His head. - sus.

Saviour of the world, thank you for dying on the cross.
All praise to You our risen Lord, Hallelujah! Jesus.

1. In the garden of Gethsemane Jesus knelt and prayed,
   For He knew the time was near when He would be betrayed.
   God gave Him the strength to cope with all that people did to hurt Him;
   Soldiers laughed and forced a crown of thorns upon His head.
   Saviour of the world . . .

2. On a cross outside the city they nailed Jesus high;
   Innocent, but still He suffered as they watched Him die.
   Nothing that the soldiers did could make Him lose control, for Jesus
   Knew the time to die then "It is finished", was His cry.
   Saviour of the world . . .

3. Three days later by God's pow'r He rose up from the dead,
   For the tomb could not hold Jesus it was as He'd said;
   Victor over sin and death He conquered Satan's power; so let us
   Celebrate that Jesus is alive for ever more.
   Saviour of the world . . .

217 Shalōm, my friend

Michael Lehr

Michael Metcalf

Gently

Sha - lōm, my__ friend, sha - lōm, my__ friend, Sha -

lōm, sha - lōm. Till we meet a - gain, till we

meet a - gain, Sha - lōm, sha - lōm.

Shalōm, my friend, shalōm, my friend,
Shalōm, shalōm.
Till we meet again, till we meet again,
Shalōm, shalōm.

Michael Lehr

218 Sing we the King

C.H. Gabriel (1856-1932)

Sing we the King who is com-ing to reign,

Glo-ry to Je-sus, the Lamb that was slain.

Life and sal-va-tion His com-ing shall bring.

Joy to all those who know Je-sus as King.

Come let us sing: Praise to our King, Je - sus our King, Je - sus our King: This is our song, who to Je - sus be - long: Glo - ry to Je - sus, to Je - sus our King.

1. Sing we the King who is coming to reign,
   Glory to Jesus, the Lamb that was slain.
   Life and salvation His coming shall bring.
   Joy to all those who know Jesus as King.

   Come let us sing: Praise to our King,
   Jesus our King, Jesus our King:
   This is our song, who to Jesus belong:
   Glory to Jesus, to Jesus our King.

2. All men who dwell in His marvellous light,
   Races long severed His love shall unite,
   Justice and truth from His sceptre shall spring,
   Wrong shall be ended when Jesus is King.
       Come let us sing . . .

3. All shall be well in His kingdom of peace,
   Freedom and wisdom and love shall not cease,
   Foe shall be friend when His triumph we sing,
   Sword shall be sickle when Jesus is King.
       Come let us sing . . .

4. Souls shall be saved from the burden of sin,
   Doubt shall not darken His witness within,
   Hell has no terrors, and death has no sting;
   Love is victorious when Jesus is King.
       Come let us sing . . .

5. Kingdom of Christ, for Your coming we pray,
   Hasten, O Father, the dawn of the day
   When this new song Your creation shall sing,
   Satan is conquered and Jesus is King.
       Come let us sing . . .

C. Silvester Horne, 1865-1914
Altered © 1986 Horrobin/Leavers

219 Silent night

STILL NACHT

F. Gruber (1787–1863)

Sil - ent night, ho - ly night! Sleeps the world;

hid from sight, Ma - ry and Jo - seph in sta - ble bare

Watched o'er the Child _ be - lov - ed and fair Sleep-ing in hea - ven-ly

rest,_____ Sleep - ing in hea - ven - ly rest._____

1. Silent night, holy night!
   Sleeps the world; hid from sight,
   Mary and Joseph in stable bare
   Watched o'er the Child beloved and fair
   Sleeping in heavenly rest,
   Sleeping in heavenly rest.

2. Silent night, holy night!
   Shepherds first saw the light;
   Heard resounding clear and long,
   Far and near, the angel song:
   'Christ the Redeemer is here',
   'Christ the Redeemer is here'.

3. Silent night, holy night!
   Son of God, O how bright
   Love is smiling from Your face!
   Strikes for us now the hour of grace,
   Saviour, since You are born,
   Saviour, since You are born.

J. Mohr, 1792–1848
tr. S. A. Brooke, 1832–1916

220 Someone's brought a loaf of bread (The harvest table)

arr. Phil Burt

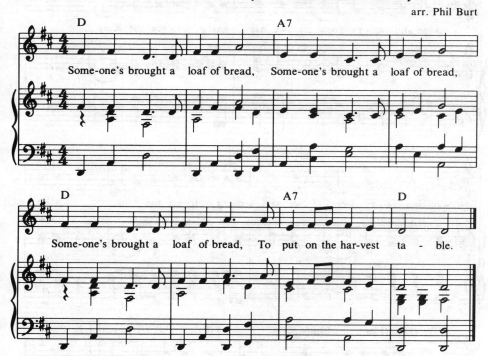

1. Someone's brought a loaf of bread,
   Someone's brought a loaf of bread,
   Someone's brought a loaf of bread,
   To put on the harvest table.

2. Someone's brought a jar of jam,
   Someone's brought a jar of jam,
   Someone's brought a jar of jam,
   To put on the harvest table.

Other verses as desired

Last verse: Thank You Lord for all your gifts,
Thank You Lord for all your gifts,
Thank You Lord for all your gifts,
To put on the harvest table.

221 Soon and very soon

Andrae Crouch

Soon and ve-ry soon__ we are going to see the King,__

Soon and ve-ry soon__ we are going to see the King,__

Soon and ve-ry soon__ we are going to see the King, Al-le-

lu - ia,__ al-le - lu - ia,__ we're going to see the King!

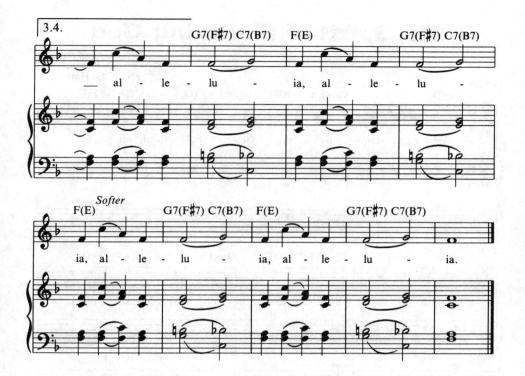

3.4.

Softer

al - le - lu - ia, al - le - lu - ia, al - le - lu - ia, al - le - lu - ia.

G7(F♯7) C7(B7) F(E) G7(F♯7) C7(B7) F(E) G7(F♯7) C7(B7) F(E) G7(F♯7) C7(B7)

1. Soon and very soon we are going to see the King,
   Soon and very soon we are going to see the King,
   Soon and very soon we are going to see the King,
   Alleluia, alleluia, we're going to see the King!

2. No more cryin' there we are going to see the King,
   No more cryin' there we are going to see the King,
   No more cryin' there we are going to see the King,
   Alleluia, alleluia, we're going to see the King!

3. No more dyin' there we are going to see the King,
   No more dyin' there we are going to see the King,
   No more dyin' there we are going to see the King,
   Alleluia, alleluia, we're going to see the King!
   Alleluia, alleluia, alleluia, alleluia.

4. Soon and very soon we are going to see the King,
   Soon and very soon we are going to see the King,
   Soon and very soon we are going to see the King,
   Alleluia, alleluia, we're going to see the King!
   Alleluia, alleluia, alleluia, alleluia.

222 Spirit of the living God

Words and music
D. Iverson
arr. W.G. Hathaway

Spirit of the living God, fall afresh on me,
Spirit of the living God, fall afresh on me:
Break me, melt me, mould me, fill me;
Spirit of the living God, fall afresh on me.

223 Surely goodness and mercy

Alfred B. Smith
and John W. Peterson

Capo 1

E(D)

Sure - ly good - ness and mer - cy shall fol - low ___ me All the days, all the days of my life; _____ Sure - ly good - ness and mer - cy shall fol - low ___ me All the

B♭7(A7)   Cm(Bm) B♭7(A7)   E♭(D)

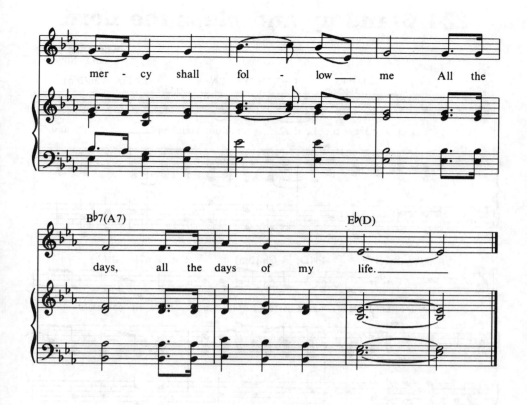

Surely goodness and mercy shall follow me
All the days, all the days of my life;
Surely goodness and mercy shall follow me
All the days, all the days of my life;
And I shall dwell in the house of the Lord forever,
And I shall feast at the table spread for me;
Surely goodness and mercy shall follow me
All the days, all the days of my life.

224 Stand up and bless the Lord

Words and music
Andy Silver

Stand up and bless the Lord your God,
Stand up and bless the Lord.
His name is exalted above all names,
Stand up and bless the Lord.
For our God is good to us,
Always ready to forgive,
He is gracious and merciful.
Slow to anger and very kind,
So, stand up and bless the Lord your God,
Stand up and bless the Lord.
So, stand up and bless the Lord your God,
Stand up.

389

225 Stand up, clap hands

Roger Dyer

Alan Forest

I look a-round and then I think oh my! The world is such a

won-der-ful place, And all be-cause of the Good Lord's grace: *Stand*

Stand up, clap hands, shout thank you, Lord,
Thank you for the world I'm in.
Stand up, clap hands, shout thank you, Lord,
For happiness and peace within.

1. I look around and the sun's in the sky,
   I look around and then I think oh my!
   The world is such a wonderful place,
   And all because of the Good Lord's grace:
   Stand up, clap hands . . .

2. I look around and the creatures I see,.
   I look around and it amazes me
   That every fox and bird and hare
   Must fit in a special place somewhere:
   Stand up, clap hands . . .

3. I look around at all the joy I've had,
   I look around and then it makes me glad
   That I can offer thanks and praise
   To Him who guides me through my days:
   Stand up, clap hands . . .

Roger Dyer

226 Stand up, stand up for Jesus

MORNING LIGHT 7 6 7 6 D   G. J. Webb (1803–1887)

Stand up, stand up for Je - sus, You sold - iers of the cross! Lift high His roy - al ban - ner, It must not suf - fer loss: From vic - tory un - to vic - tory His ar - my He shall lead___ Till e - vil is de - fea - ted And Christ is Lord in - deed.

392

1. Stand up, stand up for Jesus,
   You soldiers of the cross!
   Lift high His royal banner,
   It must not suffer loss:
   From victory unto victory
   His army He shall lead
   Till evil is defeated
   And Christ is Lord indeed.

2. Stand up, stand up for Jesus!
   The trumpet-call obey;
   Then join the mighty conflict
   In this His glorious day:
   Be strong in faith and serve Him
   Against unnumbered foes;
   Let courage rise with danger,
   And strength to strength oppose.

3. Stand up, stand up for Jesus!
   Stand in His power alone,
   For human might will fail you—
   You dare not trust your own:
   Put on the gospel armour,
   Keep watch with constant prayer;
   Where duty calls or danger
   Be never failing there.

4. Stand up, stand up for Jesus!
   The fight will not be long;
   This day the noise of battle,
   The next the victor's song:
   To everyone who conquers,
   A crown of life shall be;
   We, with the king of glory,
   Shall reign eternally.

G. Duffield, 1818-1888
© in this version *Jubilate Hymns*

227 Tell me the old, old story

76.76.D with chorus

W. H. Doane (1832–1916)

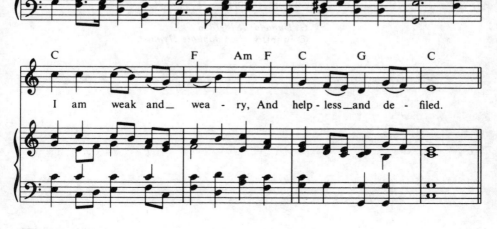

Tell me the old, old story Of un-seen things a - bove, Of
Je - sus and His glo - ry, Of Je - sus and His love.
Tell me the sto - ry sim - ply, As to a lit - tle child, For
I am weak and wea - ry, And help - less and de - filed.

394

Tell me the old, old sto - ry, Tell me the old, old sto - ry,

Tell me the old, old sto - ry, Of Je - sus and His love.

1. Tell me the old, old story
   Of unseen things above,
   Of Jesus and His glory,
   Of Jesus and His love.
   Tell me the story simply,
   As to a little child,
   For I am weak and weary,
   And helpless and defiled.

   Tell me the old, old story,
   Tell me the old, old story,
   Tell me the old, old story,
   Of Jesus and His love.

2. Tell me the story slowly,
   That I may take it in—
   That wonderful redemption,
   God's remedy for sin.
   Tell me the story often,
   For I forget so soon:
   The early dew of morning
   Has passed away at noon.
   Tell me the old, old story . . .

3. Tell me the story softly,
   With earnest tones and grave;
   Remember! I'm the sinner
   Whom Jesus came to save.
   Tell me the story always,
   If you would really be,
   In any time of trouble,
   A comforter to me.
   Tell me the old, old story . . .

4. Tell me the same old story,
   When you have cause to fear
   That this world's empty glory
   Is costing me too dear.
   Yes, and when that world's glory
   Is dawning on my soul,
   Tell me the old, old story;
   'Christ Jesus makes you whole.'
   Tell me the old, old story . . .

Arabella C. Hankey, 1834-1911, altd.

228 Tell me the stories of Jesus

STORIES OF JESUS 84.84.54.54 F. A. Challinor (1866-1952)

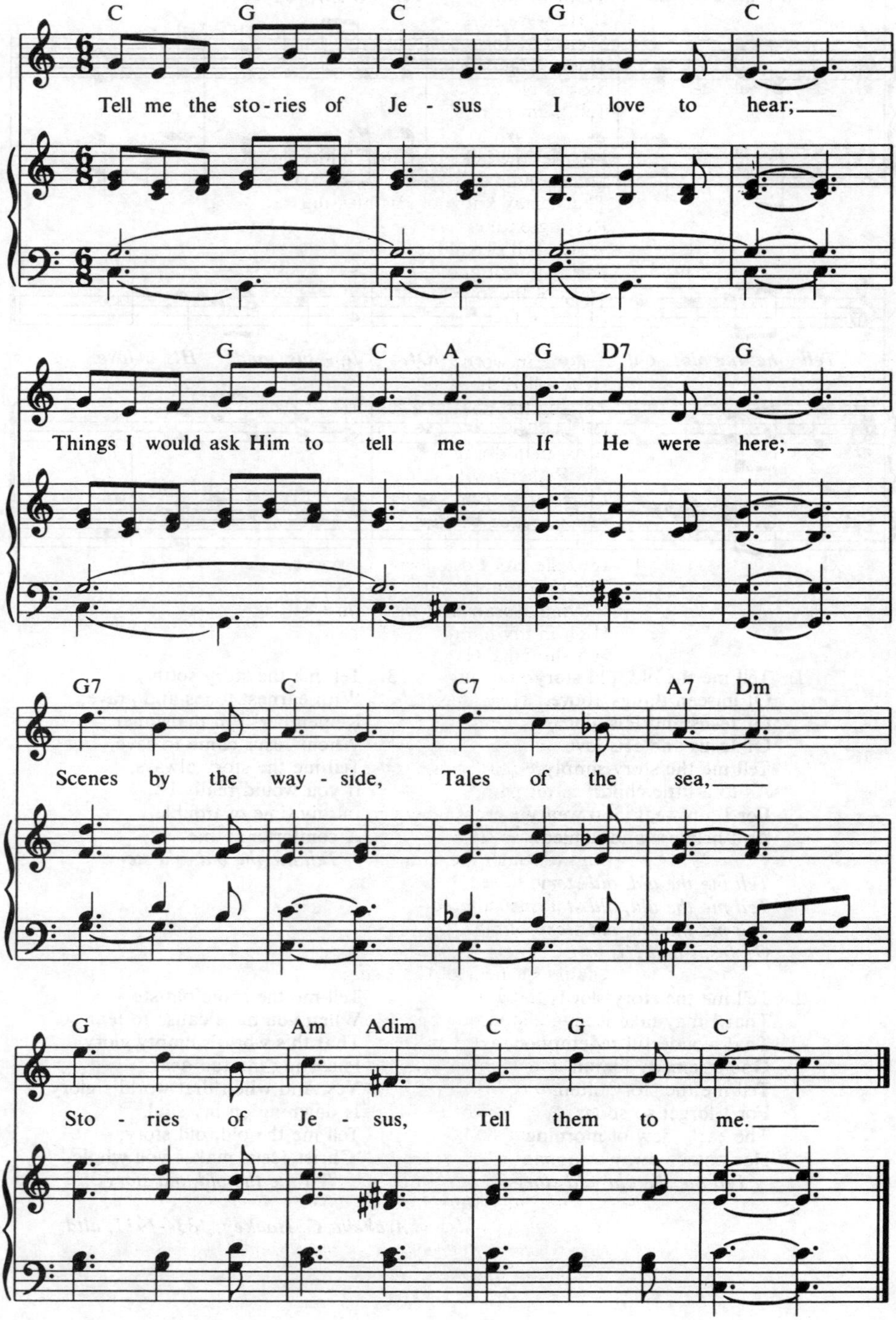

C G C G C
Tell me the sto-ries of Je - sus I love to hear;
G C A G D7 G
Things I would ask Him to tell me If He were here;
G7 C C7 A7 Dm
Scenes by the way - side, Tales of the sea,
G Am Adim C G C
Sto - ries of Je - sus, Tell them to me.

1. Tell me the stories of Jesus
   I love to hear;
   Things I would ask Him to tell me
   If He were here;
   Scenes by the wayside,
   Tales of the sea,
   Stories of Jesus,
   Tell them to me.

2. First let me hear how the children
   Stood round His knee;
   That I may know of His blessing
   Resting on me;
   Words full of kindness,
   Deeds full of grace,
   Signs of the love found
   In Jesus' face.

3. Tell me in words full of wonder,
   How rolled the sea,
   Tossing the boat in a tempest
   On Galilee
   Jesus then doing
   His Father's will,
   Ended the storm say'ng
   Peace, peace be still.

4. Into the city I'd follow
   The children's band,
   Waving a branch of the palm-tree
   High in my hand;
   Worshipping Jesus,
   Yes, I would sing
   Loudest Hosannas,
   For He is King.

5. Show me that scene in the garden,
   Of bitter pain;
   And of the cross where my Saviour
   For me was slain;
   And, through the sadness,
   Help me to see
   How Jesus suffered
   For love of me.

6. Gladly I'd hear of His rising
   Out of the grave,
   Living and strong and triumphant,
   Mighty to save;
   And how He sends us
   All men to bring
   Stories of Jesus,
   Jesus, their King.

W. H. Parker, 1845–1929, altd.
v. 6 by Hugh Martin, 1890–1964
As adapted by Horrobin/Leavers
Reproduced by permission of the National
Christian Education Council

229 Tell out my soul
(First tune)

M.A. Baughen

Tell out, my soul, the greatness of the Lord;
Un-numbered bless-ings give my spi-rit voice;
Ten-der to me the pro-mise of His Word; In
God my Sa-viour shall my heart re-joice.

1. Tell out, my soul, the greatness of the Lord;
   Unnumbered blessings give my spirit voice;
   Tender to me the promise of His Word;
   In God my Saviour shall my heart rejoice.

2. Tell out, my soul, the greatness of His name!
   Make known His might, the deeds His arm has done;
   His mercy sure, from age to age the same;
   His Holy Name — the Lord, the Mighty One.

3. Tell out, my soul, the greatness of His might!
   Powers and dominions lay their glory by.
   Proud hearts and stubborn wills are put to flight,
   The hungry fed, the humble lifted high.

4. Tell out, my soul, the glories of His word!
   Firm is His promise, and His mercy sure,
   Tell out, my soul, the greatness of the Lord
   To children's children and for evermore!

© *Timothy Dudley-Smith*

230 Thank You (simplified version)

M.G. Schneider

1. Thank You for ev'ry new good morning,
   Thank You for ev'ry fresh new day,
   Thank You that I may cast my burdens
   Wholly on to You.

2. Thank You for ev'ry friend I have, Lord,
   Thank You for ev'ry one I know,
   Thank You when I can feel forgiveness
   To my greatest foe.

3. Thank You for leisure and employment,
   Thank You for ev'ry heartfelt joy,
   Thank You for all that makes me happy,
   And for melody.

4. Thank You for ev'ry shade and sorrow,
   Thank You for comfort in Your Word,
   Thank You that I am guided by You
   Everywhere I go.

5. Thank You for grace to know Your gospel,
   Thank You for all Your Spirit's power,
   Thank You for Your unfailing love
   Which reaches far and near.

6. Thank You for free and full salvation,
   Thank You for grace to hold it fast.
   Thank You, O Lord I want to thank You
   That I'm free to thank!
   Thank You, O Lord I want to thank You
   That I'm free to thank!

M.G. Schneider
tr. and adapted by S. Lonsdale and M.A. Baughen

Thank You (full version)

M.G. Schneider
tr. and adapted by
S. Lonsdale and M.A. Baughen

M.G. Schneider
Set out in key changes by D.G. Wilson

Thank You for ev-'ry new good morn-ing, Thank You for ev-'ry fresh new day,

Thank You that I may cast my bur-dens Whol-ly on to You.

Thank You for ev-'ry friend I have, Lord, Thank You for ev-'ry one I know,

Thank You when I can feel for-give-ness To my great-est foe.

Thank You for lei-sure and em-ploy-ment, Thank You for ev-'ry heart-felt joy,

Thank You for all that makes me hap-py, And for me-lo - dy.

Thank You for ev-'ry shade and sor-row, Thank You for com-fort in Your Word,

Thank You that I am gui-ded by You Ev-ery-where I go.

Thank You for grace to know Your gos-pel, Thank You for all Your Spi-rit's power,

Thank You for Your un - fail-ing love Which reach-es far and near.

Thank You for free and full sal - va - tion, Thank You for grace to hold it fast.

Thank You, O Lord I want to thank You That I'm free to thank!___ thank!

231 Thank You, thank You Jesus

Anon.
arr. Betty Pulkingham

404

1. Thank You, thank You, Jesus.
   Thank You, thank You, Jesus.
   Thank You, thank You, Jesus, in my heart.
   Thank You, thank You, Jesus.
   Oh, thank You, thank You, Jesus.
   Thank You, thank You, Jesus, in my heart.

2. You can't make me doubt Him.
   You can't make me doubt Him.
   You can't make me doubt Him in my heart.
   You can't make me doubt Him.
   Oh, You can't make me doubt Him.
   Thank You, thank You, Jesus, in my heart.

3. I can't live without Him.
   I can't live without Him.
   I can't live without Him in my heart.
   I can't live without Him.
   Oh, I can't live without Him.
   Thank You, thank You, Jesus, in my heart.

4. Glory, hallelujah!
   Glory, hallelujah!
   Glory, hallelujah, in my heart!
   Glory, hallelujah!
   Oh, Glory, hallelujah!
   Thank You, thank You, Jesus, in my heart.

232 Thank You, Lord

Words and music
Diane Davis Andrew

- le - lu - ia,   praise the Lord!   Right __ where we   are.

1. Thank You, Lord, for this fine day,
   Thank You, Lord, for this fine day,
   Thank You, Lord, for this fine day,
   Right where we are.

   Alleluia, praise the Lord!
   Alleluia, praise the Lord!
   Alleluia, praise the Lord!
   Right where we are.

2. Thank You, Lord, for loving us,
   Thank You, Lord, for loving us,
   Thank You, Lord, for loving us,
   Right where we are.
     Alleluia, . . .

3. Thank You, Lord, for giving us peace,
   Thank You, Lord, for giving us peace,
   Thank You, Lord, for giving us peace,
   Right where we are.
     Alleluia, . . .

4. Thank You, Lord, for setting us free,
   Thank You, Lord, for setting us free,
   Thank You, Lord, for setting us free,
   Right where we are.
     Alleluia, . . .

233 Thank you God for sending Jesus

Composer unknown
arr. David Peacock

Thank You, God, for send-ing Je-sus; Thank You, Je-sus, that you came;

Ho-ly Spi-rit, won't you tell us More a-bout His won-drous name?

Thank You, God, for sending Jesus;
Thank You, Jesus, that you came;
Holy Spirit, won't you tell us
More about His wondrous name?

Copyright control

234 The best book to read

P. Bilhorn (1865–1936)

The best book to read is the Bi - ble, The best book to read is the Bi - ble; If you read it ev-'ry day it will help you on your way, Oh, the best book to read is the Bi - ble.

1. The best book to read is the Bible,
   The best book to read is the Bible;
   If you read it ev'ry day
   It will help you on your way,
   Oh, the best book to read is the Bible.

2. The best friend to have is Jesus,
   The best friend to have is Jesus;
   He will hear me when I call:
   He will keep me lest I fall,
   Oh, the best friend to have is Jesus.

3. The best thing to do is to trust Him,
   The best thing to do is to trust Him;
   And if you on Him depend,
   He will keep you to the end;
   Oh, the best thing to do is to trust Him.

235 Thank You Jesus

Words and music
Alison Huntley
arr. Roland Fudge

Capo 1

Thank You Je - sus, _____ thank You

Je - sus _____ Thank You Lord _____

_____ for lov-ing me. _____ Thank You

Je - sus, _____ thank You Je -

410

-sus   Thank You   Lord _____ for lov - ing

me. _____

1.2.   3.

1. Thank You Jesus, thank You Jesus
   Thank You Lord for loving me.
   Thank You Jesus thank You Jesus
   Thank You Lord for loving me.

2. You went to Calvary, there You died for me,
   Thank You Lord for loving me.
   You went to Calvary, there You died for me,
   Thank You Lord for loving me.

3. You rose up from the grave, to me new life You gave,
   Thank You Lord for loving me.
   You rose up from the grave, to me new life You gave,
   Thank You Lord for loving me.

4. You're coming back again, and we with You shall reign,
   Thank You Lord for loving me.
   You're coming back again, and we with You shall reign,
   Thank You Lord for loving me.

236 The day You gave us

ST. CLEMENT 9.8.9.8.

C.C. Scholefield (1839-1904)

The day You gave us, Lord, is end-ed, The sun is sink-ing in the west; To You our morn-ing hymns as-cen-ded, Your praise shall sanc-ti-fy our rest.

1. The day You gave us, Lord, is ended,
   The sun is sinking in the west;
   To You our morning hymns ascended,
   Your praise shall sanctify our rest.

2. We thank You that Your church, unsleeping
   While earth rolls onward into light,
   Through all the world her watch is keeping
   And rests not now by day or night.

3. As to each continent and island
   The dawn proclaims another day,
   The voice of prayer is never silent,
   Nor dies the sound of praise away.

4. The sun that bids us rest is waking
   Your church beneath the western sky;
   Fresh voices hour by hour are making
   Your mighty deeds resound on high.

5. So be it, Lord: Your throne shall never,
   Like earth's proud empires, pass away;
   Your kingdom stands, and grows for ever,
   Until there dawns that glorious day.

J. Ellerton, 1826-1893
© in this version *Jubilate Hymns*

237 The fields are white

Words and music
M.A. Baughen

The fields are white un-to har-vest time, Look up and see! The fields are white un-to har-vest time, Look up and see: *Pray to the Lord of the har-vest, Christ says pray.*

1. The fields are white unto harvest time,
   Look up and see!
   The fields are white unto harvest time,
   Look up and see:

   Pray to the Lord of the harvest,
   Christ says pray.
   Pray to the Lord for the workers
   Which we need in this day.

2. The harvest truly is fit to reap
   But workers few,
   The harvest truly is fit to reap
   But workers few:
       Pray to the Lord . . .

3. Who else will 'go into all the world'
   To preach the Word?
   Who else will 'go into all the world'
   To preach the Word?
       Pray to the Lord . . .

4. The Lord's return may be very soon,
   The time is short!
   The Lord's return may be very soon,
   The time is short:
       Pray to the Lord . . .

238 The first nowell

English traditional carol
arr. David Willcocks (b. 1919)

THE FIRST NOWELL Irreg.

The__ first____ now-ell the__ an-gel did say Was to Beth-le-hem's shep-herds in fields as they lay; In__ fields____ where they lay__ keep-ing their sheep On a cold win-ter's night__ that was__ so

1. The first nowell the angel did say
   Was to Bethlehem's shepherds in fields as they lay;
   In fields where they lay keeping their sheep
   On a cold winter's night that was so deep:

   Nowell, nowell, nowell, nowell,
   Born is the king of Israel!

2. Then wise men from a country far
   Looked up and saw a guiding star;
   They travelled on by night and day
   To reach the place where Jesus lay:
      Nowell, nowell, . . !

3. At Bethlehem they entered in,
   On bended knee they worshipped Him;
   They offered there in his presence
   Their gold and myrrh and frankincense:
      Nowell, nowell, . . !

4. Then let us all with one accord
   Sing praises to our heavenly Lord;
   For Christ has our salvation wrought
   And with His blood mankind has bought:
      Nowell, nowell, . . !

unknown (c. seventeenth century)
© in this version *Jubilate Hymns*

239 The greatest thing

Mark Pendergras

The great-est thing in all my life is know-ing You. The great-est thing in all my life is know-ing You. I want to know You more; I want to know You more. The

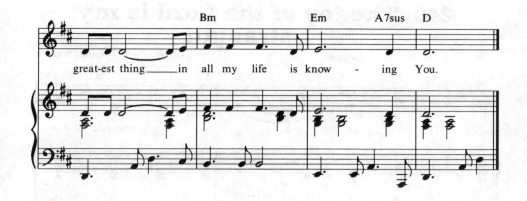

great-est thing____in all my life is know - ing You.

1. The greatest thing in all my life is knowing You.
   The greatest thing in all my life is knowing You.
   I want to know You more;
   I want to know You more.
   The greatest thing in all my life is knowing You.

2. The greatest thing in all my life is loving You.
   The greatest thing in all my life is loving You.
   I want to love You more;
   I want to love You more.
   The greatest thing in all my life is loving You.

3. The greatest thing in all my life is serving You.
   The greatest thing in all my life is serving You.
   I want to serve You more;
   I want to serve You more.
   The greatest thing in all my life is serving You.

240 The joy of the Lord is my strength

Alliene Vale
arr. Norman Warren

1. The joy of the Lord is my strength,
   The joy of the Lord is my strength,
   The joy of the Lord is my strength,
   The joy of the Lord is my strength.

2. If you want joy, you must sing for it,
   If you want joy, you must sing for it,
   If you want joy, you must sing for it,
   The joy of the Lord is my strength.

3. If you want joy, you must shout for it,
   If you want joy, you must shout for it,
   If you want joy, you must shout for it,
   The joy of the Lord is my strength.

4. If you want joy, you must jump for it,
   If you want joy, you must jump for it,
   If you want joy, you must jump for it,
   The joy of the Lord is my strength.

241 The King of love

DOMINUS REGIT ME 8.7.8.7. Iambic

J.B. Dykes (1823-1876)

The King of love my shep-herd is, Whose good-ness fails me ne-ver; I noth-ing lack if I am His And He is mine for ev-er.

1. The King of love my shepherd is,
Whose goodness fails me never;
I nothing lack if I am His
And He is mine for ever.

2. Where streams of living water flow
A ransomed soul, He leads me;
And where the fertile pastures grow,
With food from heaven feeds me.

3. Perverse and foolish I have strayed,
But in His love He sought me;
And on His shoulder gently laid,
And home, rejoicing, brought me.

4. In death's dark vale I fear no ill
With You, dear Lord, beside me;
Your rod and staff my comfort still,
Your cross before to guide me.

5. You spread a banquet in my sight
Of love beyond all knowing;
And O the gladness and delight
From Your pure chalice flowing!

6. And so through all the length of days
Your goodness fails me never;
Good Shepherd, may I sing Your praise
Within Your house for ever!

H.W. Baker, 1821-1877
© in this version *Jubilate Hymns*

421

242 The Lord has need of me

Words and music
Cecil J. Allen
arr. Phil Burt

Capo 3

The Lord has need of me, His sol-dier_ I will be; He gave Him-self my life to_ win, And so I mean to fol-low Him, And serve Him faith-ful-ly. So al-though the_ fight be fierce and long, I'll

The Lord has need of me,
His soldier I will be;
He gave Himself my life to win,
And so I mean to follow Him,
And serve Him faithfully.
So although the fight be fierce and long,
I'll carry on, He makes me strong;
And then one day His face I'll see,
And Oh! the joy when He says to me,
'Well done! My brave Crusader!'

243 The Lord's my Shepherd

CRIMOND C.M.

Melody by
Jessie S. Irvine (1836-1887)

Capo 3

The Lord's my shep - herd, I'll not want;

He makes__ me down to lie

In pas - tures green; He's lead - ing me

The qui - et wa - ters by.

1. The Lord's my shepherd, I'll not want;
   He makes me down to lie
   In pastures green; He's leading me
   The quiet waters by.

2. My soul He does restore again,
   And me to walk does make
   Within the paths of righteousness,
   E'en for His own name's sake.

3. Yes, though I walk through death's dark vale,
   Yet will I fear no ill;
   For You are with me, and Your rod
   And staff me comfort still.

4. My table You have furnishèd
   In presence of my foes;
   My head You now with oil anoint,
   And my cup overflows.

5. Goodness and mercy all my life
   Shall surely follow me;
   And in God's house for evermore
   My dwelling-place shall be.

Francis Rous, 1579-1659
revised for Scottish Psalter, 1650
Altered © 1986 Horrobin/Leavers

244 The Lord is my Shepherd

arr. Andy Silver

Capo 1

The Lord is my Shepherd,
I'll trust in Him always.
He leads me by still waters,
I'll trust in Him always.
Always, always, I'll trust in Him always,
Always, always, I'll trust in Him always.

Copyright control

245 There is a green hill

HORSLEY C.M.

W. Horsley (1774-1858)

Capo 1

1. There is a green hill far away,
   Outside a city wall,
   Where the dear Lord was crucified
   Who died to save us all.

2. We may not know, we cannot tell
   What pains He had to bear;
   But we believe it was for us
   He hung and suffered there.

3. He died that we might be forgiven,
   He died to make us good,
   That we might go at last to heaven
   Saved by His precious blood.

4. There was no other good enough
   To pay the price of sin;
   He only could unlock the gate
   Of heaven, and let us in.

5. O dearly, dearly has He loved,
   And we must love Him too,
   And trust in His redeeming blood,
   And try His works to do.

Cecil Frances Alexander, 1823-1895

246 There are hundreds of sparrows

J. Larsson

There are hun-dreds of spar-rows, thou-sands, mil-lions, They're
two a pen-ny, far too ma-ny there must be; There are
hun-dreds and thou-sands, mil-lions of spar-rows, But
God knows ev-'ry-one and God knows me.

last time only

But God knows ev - 'ry-one and God knows me.

1. There are hundreds of sparrows, thousands, millions,
   They're two a penny, far too many there must be;
   There are hundreds and thousands, millions of sparrows,
   But God knows ev'ry-one and God knows me.

2. There are hundreds of flowers, thousands, millions ,
   And flowers fair the meadows wear for all to see;
   There are hundreds and thousands, millions of flowers,
   But God knows ev'ry-one and God knows me.

3. There are hundreds of planets, thousands, millions,
   Way out in space each has a place by God's decree;
   There are hundreds and thousands, millions of planets,
   But God knows ev'ry-one and God knows me.

4. There are hundreds of children, thousands, millions ,
   And yet their names are written on God's memory,
   There are hundreds and thousands, millions of children,
   But God knows ev'ry-one and God knows me.
   But God knows ev'ry-one and God knows me.

J. Gowans

247 There's a song of exaltation

arr. Andy Silver

(boys) Sing Halle-lu-jah, (girls) Sing Halle-lu-jah, (all) Sing Halle-lu-jah, sing.

(all)   There's a song of exaltation
          Full of joy and inspiration
          Echoed down through all creation,
          Sing Hallelujah sing,

(boys) Sing Hallelujah,

(girls) Sing Hallelujah,

(boys) Sing Hallelujah,

(girls) Sing Hallelujah,

(boys) Sing Hallelujah,

(girls) Sing Hallelujah,

(all)   Sing Hallelujah sing.

248 There's a way back

Words and music
E. H. Swinstead (d. 1976)

There's a way back to God from the dark paths of sin; There's a door that is o-pen and you may go in: At Cal-va-ry's cross is where you be-gin, When you come as a sin-ner to Je-sus.

There's a way back to God from the dark paths of sin;
There's a door that is open and you may go in:
At Calvary's cross is where you begin,
When you come as a sinner to Jesus.

249 There's new life in Jesus

arr. Andy Silver

There's new life in Je - sus, Lift up your heart;

Lift up your heart, Lift up your heart,

There's new life in Je - sus, Lift up your heart.

1. There's new life in Jesus, Lift up your heart;
   There's new life in Jesus, Lift up your heart;
   Lift up your heart, Lift up your heart,
   There's new life in Jesus, Lift up your heart.

2. There is healing in His love, Lift up your heart;
   There is healing in His love, Lift up your heart;
   Lift up your heart, Lift up your heart,
   There's new life in Jesus, Lift up your heart.

3. There is joy in serving Him, Lift up your heart;
   There is joy in serving Him, Lift up your heart;
   Lift up your heart, Lift up your heart,
   There's new life in Jesus, Lift up your heart.

Copyright control

250 The steadfast love of the Lord

Words and music by
Edith McNeill

The stead-fast love of the Lord nev-er ceas-es; His mer-cies nev-er___ come to an end.___ They are new ev-'ry morning, New ev-'ry morn-ing, Great is Your faith-ful-ness, O

Lord, Great is Your faith - ful - ness. _____

The steadfast love of the Lord never ceases;
His mercies never come to an end.
They are new ev'ry morning,
New ev'ry morning,
Great is Your faithfulness, O Lord,
Great is Your faithfulness.

251 The Virgin Mary had a baby

Melody from the
Edric Connor Collection
arr. D.J. Crawshaw

The Vir-gin Ma-ry had a ba-by boy, ___ The Vir-gin Ma-ry had a ba-by boy, ___ The Vir-gin Ma-ry had a ba-by boy, And they said that His name was Je-sus.

He come from the glo-ry

1. The Virgin Mary had a baby boy,
   The Virgin Mary had a baby boy,
   The Virgin Mary had a baby boy,
   And they said that His name was Jesus.

   He come from the glory
   He come from the glorious kingdom;
   He come from the glory
   He come from the glorious kingdom;
   Oh, yes! believer.
   Oh, yes! believer.
   He come from the glory
   He come from the glorious kingdom.

2. The angels sang when the baby was born,
   The angels sang when the baby was born,
   The angels sang when the baby was born,
   And proclaimed Him the Saviour Jesus.
   He come from . . .

3. The wise men saw where the baby was born,
   The wise men saw where the baby was born,
   The wise men saw where the baby was born,
   And they saw that His name was Jesus.
   He come from . . .

252 The wise man built his house upon the rock

arr. Phil Burt

The wise man built his house up-on the rock.___ The wise man built his house up-on the rock.___ The wise man built his house up-on the rock And the rain came tum-bling down.___ And the rain came down and the floods came up,___ The

rain came down and the floods came up,___ The rain came down and the

floods came up, And the house on the rock stood firm._____

The wise man built his house upon the rock.
The wise man built his house upon the rock.
The wise man built his house upon the rock
And the rain came tumbling down.
And the rain came down and the floods came up,
The rain came down and the floods came up,
The rain came down and the floods came up,
And the house on the rock stood firm.

The foolish man built his house upon the sand.
The foolish man built his house upon the sand.
The foolish man built his house upon the sand
And the rain came tumbling down.
And the rain came down and the floods came up,
The rain came down and the floods came up,
The rain came down and the floods came up,
And the house on the sand fell flat.

Copyright control

253 The wise may bring their learning

TYROLESE 76.76.D.

Tyrolese Carol.

The wise may bring their learn - ing, The rich may bring their wealth, And some may bring their great - ness, And some their strength and health: We too would bring our trea - sures To of - fer to the King; We

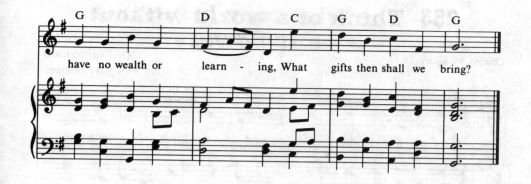

have no wealth or learn - ing, What gifts then shall we bring?

1. The wise may bring their learning,
   The rich may bring their wealth,
   And some may bring their greatness,
   And some their strength and health:
   We too would bring our treasures
   To offer to the King;
   We have no wealth or learning,
   What gifts then shall we bring?

2. We'll bring the many duties
   We have to do each day;
   We'll try our best to please Him,
   At home, at school, at play:
   And better are these treasures
   To offer to the King;
   Than richest gifts without them;
   Yet these we all may bring.

3. We'll bring Him hearts that love Him,
   We'll bring Him thankful praise,
   And lives for ever striving
   To follow in His ways:
   And these shall be the treasures
   We offer to the King,
   And these are gifts that ever
   Our grateful hearts may bring.

Book of Praise for Children, 1881, altd.

254 Think of a world without any flowers

Doreen Newport

Graham Westcott
arr. Douglas Coombes

Think of a world with - out a - ny flow - ers, Think of a world with - out a - ny trees, Think of a sky with - out a - ny sun - shine, Think of the air with - out a - ny breeze. We thank You, Lord, for flow'rs and trees and sunshine, We thank You, Lord, and praise Your Ho - ly Name.

1. Think of a world without any flowers,
   Think of a world without any trees,
   Think of a sky without any sunshine,
   Think of the air without any breeze.
   We thank You, Lord, for flow'rs and trees and sunshine,
   We thank You, Lord, and praise Your Holy Name.

2. Think of a world without any animals,
   Think of a field without any herd,
   Think of a stream without any fishes,
   Think of a dawn without any bird.
   We thank You, Lord, for all Your living creatures,
   We thank You, Lord, and praise Your Holy Name.

3. Think of a world without any people,
   Think of a street with no one living there,
   Think of a town without any houses,
   No one to love and nobody to care.
   We thank You, Lord, for families and friendships,
   We thank You, Lord, and praise Your Holy Name.

Doreen Newport

255 This is the day

Les Garrett
Fiji Island Folk
Melody
arr. Roland Fudge

Joyfully

E

This is the day, This is the day that the

B7

Lord has made, That the Lord has made.

E

We will rejoice, We will rejoice and be glad in it, And be

A   E

glad in it. This is the day that the Lord has made

We will rejoice and be glad in __ it. This is the day,

This is the day that the Lord has made.

1. This is the day,
   This is the day that the Lord has made,
   That the Lord has made.
   We will rejoice,
   We will rejoice and be glad in it
   And be glad in it.
   This is the day that the Lord has made
   We will rejoice and be glad in it.
   This is the day,
   This is the day that the Lord has made.

2. This is the day,
   This is the day when He rose again,
   When He rose again,
   We will rejoice,
   We will rejoice and be glad in it,
   And be glad in it.
   This is the day when He rose again.
   We will rejoice and be glad in it.
   This is the day,
   This is the day when He rose again.

3. This is the day,
   This is the day when the Spirit came,
   When the Spirit came,
   We will rejoice,
   We will rejoice and be glad in it,
   And be glad in it.
   This is the day when the Spirit came.
   We will rejoice and be glad in it.
   This is the day,
   This is the day when the Spirit came.

256 This joyful Eastertide

VRUECHTEN

17th-century Dutch melody

Capo 2

This joy - ful Eas - ter - tide, What need is there for griev - - ing? Cast all your care a - side And be not un - be - liev - - ing: *Come, share our Eas - ter joy That death could*

1. This joyful Eastertide,
   What need is there for grieving?
   Cast all your care aside
   And be not unbelieving:

   Come, share our Easter joy
   That death could not imprison,
   Nor any power destroy,
   Our Christ, who is arisen,
   Arisen, arisen, arisen!

2. No work for Him is vain,
   No faith in Him mistaken,
   For Easter makes it plain
   His Kingdom is not shaken:
       Come, share our Easter joy . . .

3. Then put your trust in Christ,
   In waking or in sleeping.
   His grace on earth sufficed;
   He'll never quit His keeping:
       Come, share our Easter joy . . .

Fred Pratt Green, b. 1903
© *Stainer & Bell Ltd.*
Reprinted by permission

257 Though the world has forsaken God

THEY ARE WATCHING YOU

R.T. Bewes
arr. M.C.T. Strover

Though the world has for-sa-ken God,— Treads a diff - 'rent path,— lives a diff - 'rent way,— I walk the road that the Sav-iour trod, And all may know I live un - der Je - sus' sway: *They are watch-ing you,— mark-ing all you do,*

Hear-ing the things you say; Let them see the Sav - iour as He

shines in you, Let His pow'r con-trol you ev - 'ry day.

1. Though the world has forsaken God,
   Treads a diff'rent path, lives a diff'rent way,
   I walk the road that the Saviour trod,
   And all may know I live under Jesus' sway:

   They are watching you, marking all you do,
   Hearing the things you say;
   Let them see the Saviour as He shines in you,
   Let His pow'r control you ev'ry day.

2. Men will look at the life I lead,
   See the side I take, and the things I love;
   They judge my Lord by my every deed—
   Lord, set my affections on things above:
     They are watching you . . .

3. When assailed in temptation's hour,
   By besetting sins, by the fear of man,
   Then I can know Jesus' mighty power,
   And become like Him in His perfect plan:
     They are watching you . . .

4. Here on earth people walk in the night;
   With no lamp to guide, they are dead in sin;
   I know the Lord Who can give them light,
   I live, yet not I, but Christ within:
     They are watching you . . .

258 This little light of mine

Words and melody
Traditional

This lit-tle light of mine, I'm gon-na let it shine, This lit-tle light of mine, I'm gon-na let it shine, This lit-tle light of mine, I'm gon-na let it shine, Let it shine, let it shine, let it shine.

The light that shines is the light of love,
Lights the dark-ness from a - bove. It shines on me and it
shines on you, And shows what the pow-er of love can do. I'm gon-na
shine my light both far and near, I'm gon-na shine my light both

bright and clear.___ Where there's a dark cor - ner

D.C. al Fine

in this land___ I'm gon-na let my lit - tle light shine.

This little light of mine, I'm gonna let it shine,
This little light of mine, I'm gonna let it shine,
This little light of mine, I'm gonna let it shine,
Let it shine, let it shine, let it shine.

1. The light that shines is the light of love,
   Lights the darkness from above.
   It shines on me and it shines on you,
   And shows what the power of love can do.
   I'm gonna shine my light both far and near,
   I'm gonna shine my light both bright and clear.
   Where there's a dark corner in this land
   I'm gonna let my little light shine.
   This little light of mine . . .

2. On Monday He gave me the gift of love,
   Tuesday, peace came from above.
   On Wednesday He told me to have more faith,
   On Thursday He gave me a little more grace.
   Friday, He told me just to watch and pray,
   Saturday, He told me just what to say.
   On Sunday He gave me the power divine
   To let my little light shine.
   This little light of mine . . .

259 To God be the glory!

W. H. Doane (1832–1916)

Capo 1

To God be the glo-ry! Great things He has done! So loved He the world that He gave us His Son; Who yield-ed His life an a-tone-ment for sin, And op-ened the life gate that all may go in.

1. To God be the glory! Great things He has done!
   So loved He the world that He gave us His Son;
   Who yielded His life an atonement for sin,
   And opened the life gate that all may go in.

   Praise the Lord! Praise the Lord! Let the earth hear His voice!
   Praise the Lord! Praise the Lord! Let the people rejoice!
   O come to the Father, through Jesus the Son:
   And give Him the glory! Great things He has done!

2. O perfect redemption, the purchase of blood!
   To every believer the promise of God;
   The vilest offender who truly believes,
   That moment from Jesus a pardon receives.
       Praise the Lord! . . .

3. Great things He has taught us, great things He has done,
   And great our rejoicing through Jesus the Son;
   But purer, and higher, and greater will be
   Our wonder, our rapture, when Jesus we see.
       Praise the Lord! . . .

Frances van Alstyne, 1820-1915

260 Turn your eyes upon Jesus

Words and music by
Helen Lemmel

Turn your eyes up-on Je - sus, Look full in His won-der-ful face;_____ And the things of earth will grow strange - ly dim In the light of His glo-ry and grace.___

Turn your eyes upon Jesus,
Look full in His wonderful face;
And the things of earth will grow strangely dim
In the light of His glory and grace.

Keep your eyes upon Jesus,
Let nobody else take His place;
So that hour by hour you will know His power
Till at last you have run the great race.

261 Twelve men went to spy in Canaan

arr. Andy Silver

Twelve men went to spy in Ca-naan, Ten were bad, two were good.

What did they see when they spied in Ca-naan? Ten were bad, two were good.

Some saw gi-ants tough and tall, Some saw grapes in clus-ters fall,

Some saw God was in it all,— Ten were bad, two were good.

Twelve men went to spy in Canaan,
Ten were bad, two were good.
What did they see when they spied in Canaan?
Ten were bad, two were good.
Some saw giants tough and tall,
Some saw grapes in clusters fall,
Some saw God was in it all,
Ten were bad, two were good.

457

© 1945 Hugh Mitchell

262 Two little eyes

Words and music
C.C. Kerr

Two little eyes to look to God,
Two little ears to hear His Word,
Two little feet to walk in His ways,
Two little lips to sing His praise,
Two little hands to do His will,
And one little heart to love Him still.

263 Unto us a Boy is born

PUER NOBIS 7 6 7 6

German carol melody
harm. Geoffrey Shaw (1879–1943)

From *The Oxford Book of Carols* by permission of Oxford University Press.

1. Unto us a Boy is born!
   King of all creation,
   Came He to a world forlorn
   The Lord of every nation,
   The Lord of every nation.

2. Cradled in a stall was He
   With sleepy cows and asses;
   But the very beasts could see
   That He all men surpasses,
   That He all men surpasses,

3. Herod then with fear was filled:
   'A prince,' he said, 'in Jewry!'
   All the little boys he killed
   At Bethlehem in his fury,
   At Bethlehem in his fury.

4. Now may Mary's Son, who came
   So long ago to love us,
   Lead us all with hearts aflame
   Unto the joys above us,
   Unto the joys above us.

5. Alpha and Omega He!
   Let the organ thunder,
   While the choir with peals of glee
   Doth rend the air asunder!
   Doth rend the air asunder!

German (15th century) tr. Percy Dearmer, 1867–1936
© *1964 Oxford University Press*

264 We have a king who rides a donkey

WHAT SHALL WE DO

We have a king who rides a don-key, We have a king who rides a don-key,

We have a king who rides a don-key And his name is Je - sus.

Je - sus, the king, is ris - en, Je - sus, the king, is ris - en,

Je - sus, the king, is ris - en Ear - ly in the morn - ing.

1. We have a king who rides a donkey,
   We have a king who rides a donkey,
   We have a king who rides a donkey
   And his name is Jesus.

   Jesus, the king, is risen,
   Jesus, the king, is risen,
   Jesus, the king, is risen
   Early in the morning.

2. Trees are waving a royal welcome,
   Trees are waving a royal welcome,
   Trees are waving a royal welcome
   For the king called Jesus.
     Jesus, the king, is risen . . .

3. We have a king who cares for people,
   We have a king who cares for people,
   We have a king who cares for people
   And his name is Jesus.
     Jesus, the king, is risen . . .

4. What shall we do with our life this morning?
   What shall we do with our life this morning?
   What shall we do with our life this morning?
   Give it up in service!
     Jesus, the king, is risen . . .

Fred Kaan
Copyright © Stainer & Bell Ltd.
Reprinted with permission.

265 We love to praise You Jesus

Capo 3

Phil Burt

1. We love to praise You Jesus,
   We love to tell You
   That You are Lord, that You are Lord.

2. We love to know You Jesus,
   We love to hear You
   Say we are Yours, say we are Yours.

3. We want to thank You Jesus,
   For giving Your life
   So we can live, so we can live.

© *1986 Margaret Westworth*

461

266 We have heard

LIMPSFIELD 73.73.77.73.

Josiah Booth (1852-1929)

We have heard a joy- ful sound! Je - sus
saves! ___ Spread the glad - ness all___ a - round:
Je - sus saves! ___ Words of life for
ev - ery land, Must be sent a - cross___ the waves;

Onward! 'tis our Lord's command: Je - sus saves!

1. We have heard a joyful sound!
   Jesus saves!
   Spread the gladness all around:
   Jesus saves!
   Words of life for every land,
   Must be sent across the waves;
   Onward! 'tis our Lord's command:
   Jesus saves!

2. Sing above the toils of life:
   Jesus saves!
   He is with us in the strife:
   Jesus saves!
   Sing the truth, He died yet lives,
   Strength'ning me through all my days.
   Sing in triumph! Life He gives:
   Jesus saves!

3. Let the nations hear God's voice:
   Jesus saves!
   So that they can then rejoice:
   Jesus saves!
   Shout salvation full and free
   That ev'ry land may hear God's praise
   This our song of victory:
   Jesus saves!

Priscilla Ownes, 1829-1907
Altered © 1986 Horrobin/Leavers.

267 We plough the fields

WIR PFLÜGEN 76.76.D with chorus

J.A.P. Schulz (1747-1800)

We plough the fields and scat-ter The good seed on the land, But
it is fed and wat-ered By God's al-migh-ty hand; He
sends the snow in win-ter, The warmth to swell the grain, The
breez-es and the sun-shine And soft re-fresh-ing rain.

All good gifts a-round us Are sent from heaven a-bove, Then

thank the Lord, O thank the Lord, For all_____ His love.

1. We plough the fields and scatter
   The good seed on the land,
   But it is fed and watered
   By God's almighty hand;
   He sends the snow in winter,
   The warmth to swell the grain,
   The breezes and the sunshine
   And soft refreshing rain.

   All good gifts around us
   Are sent from heaven above,
   Then thank the Lord, O thank the Lord,
   For all His love.

2. He only is the Maker
   Of all things near and far;
   He paints the wayside flower,
   He lights the evening star;
   The wind and waves obey Him,
   By Him the birds are fed;
   Much more to us, His children,
   He gives our daily bread.
      All good gifts . . .

3. We thank You then, O Father,
   For all things bright and good,
   The seed-time and the harvest,
   Our life, our health, our food.
   Accept the gifts we offer
   For all Your love imparts,
   We come now Lord to give you
   Our humble, thankful hearts.
      All good gifts . . .

Matthias Claudius, 1740-1815
tr. Jane Montgomery Campbell, 1817-1878
Altered © 1986 Horrobin/Leavers

268 We really want to thank You

Words and music
Ed Baggett
arr. Betty Pulkingham

Capo 2   **With a swing**

We real - ly want to thank You Lord.

We real - ly want to bless Your name.   Hal-le - lu - jah!

last time

Je - sus is ___ our king!

1.

2.   We thank You Lord, for Your gift to us, ___ Your

life so rich be - yond com-pare, The gift of Your bo - dy

here on __ earth Of which we sing and share. __

D.C.

✛ *CODA*

king! __

We really want to thank You Lord.
We really want to bless Your name.
Hallelujah! Jesus is our king!
We really want to thank You Lord.
We really want to bless Your name.
Hallelujah! Jesus is our king!

1. We thank You Lord, for Your gift to us,
   Your life so rich beyond compare,
   The gift of Your body here on earth
   Of which we sing and share.
       We really want to thank . . .

2. We thank You Lord, for our life together,
   To live and move in the love of Christ,
   Your tenderness which sets us free
   To serve You with our lives.
       We really want to thank . . .

3. Praise God from whom all blessings flow,
   Praise Him all creatures here below,
   Praise Him above you heavenly host,
   Praise Father, Son and Holy Ghost.
       We really want to thank . . .

467

269 Were you there

American Folk Hymn Melody
arr. Francis Westbrook (1904-1975)

Were you there when they cru-ci-fied my Lord?_____

_ Were you there when they cru-ci-fied my

Lord?_____ Oh!_____

Some-times it caus-es me to trem-ble, trem-ble,

trem - ble; Were you there when they cru - ci - fied my Lord?

1. Were you there when they crucified my Lord?
   Were you there when they crucified my Lord?
   Oh! Sometimes it causes me to tremble, tremble, tremble;
   Were you there when they crucified my Lord?

2. Were you there when they nailed Him to the tree?
   Were you there when they nailed Him to the tree?
   Oh! Sometimes it causes me to tremble, tremble, tremble;
   Were you there when they nailed Him to the tree?

3. Were you there when they laid Him in the tomb?
   Were you there when they laid Him in the tomb?
   Oh! Sometimes it causes me to tremble, tremble, tremble;
   Were you there when they laid Him in the tomb?

4. Were you there when God raised Him from the dead?
   Were you there when God raised Him from the dead?
   Oh! Sometimes it causes me to tremble, tremble, tremble;
   Were you there when God raised Him from the dead?

270 We shall overcome

Zilphia Horton, Frank Hamilton,
Guy Carawan, Pete Seeger
arr. D.G. Wilson

We shall ov - er - come, ____ We shall ov - er - come, ____ We shall ov - er - come some day; ____ By faith in Christ I do be - lieve

We shall ov – er – come some day.

1. We shall overcome,
   We shall overcome,
   We shall overcome some day;
   By faith in Christ I do believe
   We shall overcome some day.

2. The truth will make us free,
   The truth will make us free,
   The truth will make us free some day;
   By faith in Christ I do believe
   We shall overcome some day.

3. The Lord will see us through,
   The Lord will see us through,
   The Lord will see us through some day.
   By faith in Christ I do believe
   We shall overcome some day.

4. We shall live in peace,
   We shall live in peace,
   We shall live in peace some day;
   By faith in Christ I do believe
   We shall overcome some day.

5. We shall overcome,
   We shall overcome,
   We shall overcome some day;
   By faith in Christ I do believe
   We shall overcome some day.

271 We three kings of Orient

Words and music
J. H. Hopkins Jr (1820–1891)

We three kings of Or - i - ent are; Bear - ing
gifts we tra - vel a - far, Field and foun - tain, moor and
moun - tain, Fol - low - ing yon - der star: O____
star of won - der, star of night, Star with

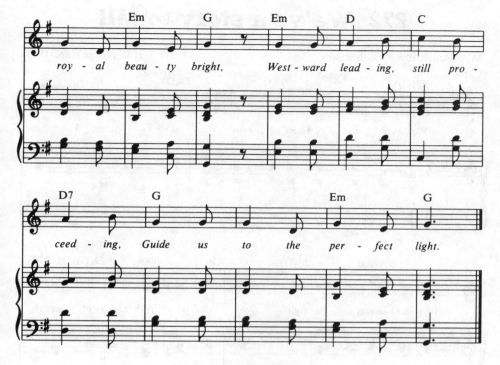

roy - al beau - ty bright, West - ward lead - ing, still pro - ceed - ing, Guide us to the per - fect light.

1. We three kings of Orient are;
   Bearing gifts we travel afar,
   Field and fountain, moor and mountain,
   Following yonder star:

   O star of wonder, star of night,
   Star with royal beauty bright,
   Westward leading, still proceeding,
   Guide us to the perfect light.

2. Born a King on Bethlehem plain,
   Gold I bring, to crown Him again—
   King for ever, ceasing never,
   Over us all to reign:
      O star of wonder, . . .

3. Frankincense for Jesus have I,
   God on earth yet Priest on high;
   Prayer and praising all men raising
   Worship is earth's reply.
      O star of wonder, . . .

4. Myrrh is mine; its bitter perfume
   Tells of His death and Calvary's gloom;
   Sorrowing, sighing, bleeding, dying,
   Sealed in a stone-cold tomb:
      O star of wonder, . . .

5. Glorious now, behold Him arise,
   King, and God, and sacrifice:
   Heaven sings 'Alleluia',
   'Alleluia' the earth replies:
      O star of wonder, . . .

J. H. Hopkins Jr, 1820–1891
Altered © 1986 Horrobin/Leavers

473

272 We've a story to tell

MESSAGE 10.8.87 with chorus

H.E. Nichol (1862-1926)

We've a sto - ry to tell to the na - tions, That shall turn their hearts to the right, A sto - ry of truth and sweet - ness, A sto - ry of peace and light:_____ A sto - ry of peace and light: For the dark - ness shall turn to dawn - ing, And the

dawn-ing to noon-day bright, And Christ's great king-dom shall

come on earth, The king-dom of love and light.

1. We've a story to tell to the nations,
   That shall turn their hearts to the right,
   A story of truth and sweetness,
   A story of peace and light:

   For the darkness shall turn to dawning,
   And the dawning to noon-day bright,
   And Christ's great kingdom shall come on earth,
   The kingdom of love and light.

2. We've a song to be sung to the nations,
   That shall lift their hearts to the Lord;
   A song that shall conquer evil,
   So love will replace the sword:
   For the darkness shall . . .

3. We've a message to give to the nations,
   That the Lord who's reigning above
   Has sent us His Son to save us,
   And show us that God is love:
   For the darkness shall . . .

4. We've a Saviour to show to the nations,
   Who the path of sorrow has trod,
   That all of the world may listen
   And learn of the truth of God:
   For the darkness shall . . .

Colin Sterne, 1862-1926
Altered © 1986 Horrobin/Leavers

273 What a friend we have in Jesus

CONVERSE 87.87.D

C.C. Converse (1832-1918)

Capo 1

What a friend we have in Je - sus, All our sins and griefs to bear! What a pri - vi - lege to car - ry Eve - ry-thing to God in prayer! O what peace we of - ten for - feit, O what need-less pain we bear

All be-cause we do not car - ry Eve - ry-thing to God in prayer!

1. What a friend we have in Jesus,
   All our sins and griefs to bear!
   What a privilege to carry
   Everything to God in prayer!
   O what peace we often forfeit,
   O what needless pain we bear—
   All because we do not carry
   Everything to God in prayer!

2. Have we trials and temptations?
   Is there trouble anywhere?
   We should never be discouraged:
   Take it to the Lord in prayer!
   Can we find a friend so faithful,
   Who will all our sorrows share?
   Jesus knows our every weakness—
   Take it to the Lord in prayer!

3. Are we weak and heavy-laden,
   Burdened with a load of care?
   Jesus only is our refuge,
   Take it to the Lord in prayer!
   Do your friends despise, forsake you?
   Take it to the Lord in prayer!
   In His arms He'll take and shield you,
   You will find His comfort there.

Joseph Scriven, 1819-1886
Altered © 1986 Horrobin/Leavers

274 What a wonderful Saviour is Jesus

Traditional

Brightly

What a won-der-ful Sav-iour is Je-sus,___ What a won-der-ful Friend is He, For He left all the glo-ry of hea-ven, Came to earth to die on Cal-va-ry: *Sing Ho-san-na! Sing Ho-san-na! Sing Ho-san-na to the King of kings!*

1. What a wonderful Saviour is Jesus,
   What a wonderful Friend is He,
   For He left all the glory of heaven,
   Came to earth to die on Calvary:

   Sing Hosanna! Sing Hosanna!
   Sing Hosanna to the King of kings!
   Sing Hosanna! Sing Hosanna!
   Sing Hosanna to the King.

2. He arose from the grave, Hallelujah,
   And He lives never more to die,
   At the Father's right hand interceding
   He will hear and heed our faintest cry:
       Sing Hosanna! . . .

3. He is coming some day to receive us,
   We'll be caught up to heaven above,
   What a joy it will be to behold Him,
   Sing forever of His grace and love.
       Sing Hosanna! . . .

275 When I needed a neighbour

Words and music
Sydney Carter (b. 1915)

NEIGHBOURS

When I needed a neighbour, were you there, were you there? When I need-ed a neighbour, were you there?

And the creed and the co-lour and the name won't matter, Were you there?

I was

1. When I needed a neighbour, were you there, were you there?
   When I needed a neighbour, were you there?

   And the creed and the colour and the name won't matter,
   Were you there?

2. I was hungry and thirsty, were you there, were you there?
   I was hungry and thirsty, were you there?
   And the creed . . .

3. I was cold, I was naked, were you there, were you there?
   I was cold, I was naked, were you there?
   And the creed . . .

4. When I needed a shelter, were you there, were you there?
   When I needed a shelter, were you there?
   And the creed . . .

5. When I needed a healer, were you there, were you there?
   When I needed a healer, were you there?
   And the creed . . .

6. Wherever you travel, I'll be there, I'll be there,
   Wherever you travel, I'll be there,
   And the creed . . .

Sydney Carter, b. 1915

276 When Israel was in Egypt's land

GO DOWN MOSES

Negro spiritual
arr. Michael Metcalfe

When Is-rael was in E-gypt's land, *Let my peo-ple go;* Op-pressed so hard they could not stand, *Let my people go.* Go down, Mo-ses, way down in E-gypt's land; *Tell old* Phar-aoh to let my peo-ple go.

1. When Israel was in Egypt's land,
   Let my people go;
   Oppressed so hard they could not stand,
   Let my people go.

   Go down, Moses, way down in Egypt's land;
   Tell old Pharaoh to let my people go.

2. The Lord told Moses what to do,
   Let my people go;
   To lead the children of Israel through,
   Let my people go.
      Go down, Moses . . .

3. Your foes shall not before you stand,
   Let my people go;
   And you'll possess fair Canaan's land,
   Let my people go.
      Go down, Moses . . .

4. O let us from all bondage flee,
   Let my people go;
   And let us all in Christ be free,
   Let my people go.
      Go down, Moses . . .

5. I do believe without a doubt,
   Let my people go;
   That a Christian has a right to shout,
   Let my people go.
      Go down, Moses . . .

Negro Spiritual adapted Peter D. Smith, b. 1938

277 When I survey

ROCKINGHAM L.M.

E. Miller (1735–1807)

Capo 1

When I___ sur-vey the won-drous cross On which the
Prince of Glo-ry died,___ My rich-est gain I
count but loss, And pour con-tempt on all___ my pride.

1. When I survey the wondrous cross
   On which the Prince of Glory died,
   My richest gain I count but loss,
   And pour contempt on all my pride.

2. Forbid it, Lord, that I should boast,
   Save in the death of Christ my God:
   All the vain things that charm me most,
   I sacrifice them to His blood.

3. See from His head, His hands, His feet,
   Sorrow and love flow mingled down:
   Did e'er such love and sorrow meet,
   Or thorns compose so rich a crown?

4. Were the whole realm of nature mine,
   That were an offering far too small,
   Love so amazing, so divine,
   Demands my soul, my life, my all.

Isaac Watts, 1674-1748

278 When morning gilds the skies

LAUDES DOMINI 6 6.6. D.

J. Barnby (1838-1896)

1. When morning gilds the skies,
   My heart awakening cries:
   May Jesus Christ be praised!
   Alike at work and prayer
   I know my Lord is there:
   May Jesus Christ be praised!

2. When sadness fills my mind,
   My strength in Him I find:
   May Jesus Christ be praised!
   When earthly hopes grows dim
   My comfort is in Him:
   May Jesus Christ be praised!

3. The night becomes as day
   When from the heart we say:
   May Jesus Christ be praised!
   The powers of darkness fear
   When this glad song they hear:
   May Jesus Christ be praised!

4. Be this, while life is mine,
   My canticle divine:
   May Jesus Christ be praised!
   Be this the eternal song
   Through all the ages long:
   May Jesus Christ be praised!

from the German (nineteenth century)
E. Caswall, 1814-1878
© in this version *Jubilate Hymns*

279 When the road is rough

Words and music
Norman J. Clayton

When the road is rough and steep, Fix your eyes upon Je - sus,

He a - lone has pow'r to keep, Fix your eyes upon Him;

Je - sus is a gra-cious friend, One on whom you can de-pend,

He is faith - ful to the end, Fix your eyes upon Him.

When the road is rough and steep,
Fix your eyes upon Jesus,
He alone has pow'r to keep,
Fix your eyes upon Him;

Jesus is a gracious friend,
One on whom you can depend,
He is faithful to the end,
Fix your eyes upon Him.

280 When the Lord in glory comes

GLORIOUS COMING 77 77 77 D

Michael Baughen (b. 1930)
and D.G. Wilson (b. 1940)

Lively

When the Lord in glo - ry comes

Not the trumpets, not the drums, Not the anthem, not the

psalm, Not the thun - der, not the calm,

Not the shout the heavens raise, Not the chorus, not the

487

praise, Not the si - len - ces sub - lime,
Not the sounds of space and time, But His voice when He ap -
pears Shall be mu - sic to my ears — But His
voice when He ap - pears Shall be mu - sic

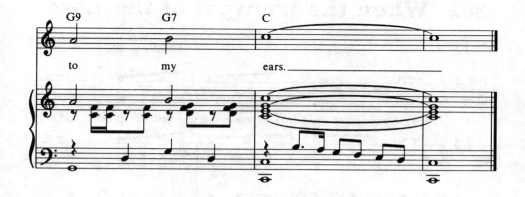

to my ears.

1. When the Lord in glory comes
   Not the trumpets, not the drums,
   Not the anthem, not the psalm,
   Not the thunder, not the calm,
   Not the shout the heavens raise,
   Not the chorus, not the praise,
   Not the silences sublime,
   Not the sounds of space and time,
   But His voice when He appears
   Shall be music to my ears—
   But His voice when He appears
   Shall be music to my ears.

2. When the Lord is seen again
   Not the glories of His reign,
   Not the lightnings through the storm,
   Not the radiance of His form,
   Not His pomp and power alone,
   Not the splendours of His throne,
   Not His robe and diadems,
   Not the gold and not the gems,
   But His face upon my sight
   Shall be darkness into light—
   But His face upon my sight
   Shall be darkness into light.

3. When the Lord to human eyes
   Shall bestride our narrow skies,
   Not the child of humble birth,
   Not the carpenter of earth,
   Not the man by all denied,
   Not the victim crucified,
   But the God who died to save,
   But the victor of the grave,
   He it is to whom I fall,
   Jesus Christ, my All in all—
   He it is to whom I fall,
   Jesus Christ, my All in all.

© *Timothy Dudley-Smith*

281 When the trumpet of the Lord

ROLL CALL

Words and music
James M. Black (1856-1938)

When the trum-pet of the Lord shall sound, and time shall be no more, And the
morn - ing breaks, e - ter - nal, bright, and fair; When the
saved of earth shall gath - er ov - er on the o - ther shore And the
roll is called up yon-der, I'll be there. *When the roll _____ is called up*

490

1. When the trumpet of the Lord shall sound, and time shall be no more,
   And the morning breaks, eternal, bright, and fair;
   When the saved of earth shall gather over on the other shore
   And the roll is called up yonder, I'll be there.

   When the roll is called up yonder,
   When the roll is called up yonder,
   When the roll is called up yonder,
   When the roll is called up yonder, I'll be there.

2. On that bright and cloudless morning when the dead in Christ shall rise,
   And the glory of his resurrection share;
   When His chosen ones shall gather to their home beyond the skies,
   And the roll is called up yonder, I'll be there.
      When the roll . . .

3. Let us labour for the Master from the dawn till setting sun,
   Let us talk of all His wond'rous love and care;
   Then when all of life is over, and our work on earth is done,
   And the roll is called up yonder, I'll be there.
      When the roll . . .

282 Wherever I am

Composer unknown
arr. David Peacock

Wher - e - ver I am I'll praise him, When-e - ver I can I'll praise him; For his love sur - rounds me like a sea; _____ I'll praise the name of Je - sus, Lift up the name of

492

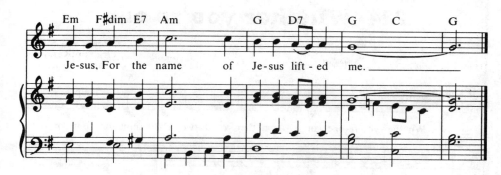

| Em F#dim E7 Am | G | D7 | G C | G |

Je-sus, For the name of Je-sus lift-ed me.

Wherever I am I'll praise him,
Whenever I can I'll praise him;
For his love surrounds me like a sea;
I'll praise the name of Jesus,
Lift up the name of Jesus,
For the name of Jesus lifted me.

Copyright control

283 Wherever I am I will praise You Lord

Greg Leavers
arr. Phil Burt

Where-ver I am I will praise You Lord, Praise You Lord. Wher-
e - ver I am Your Spi-rit fills my life with song.

1. Wherever I am I will praise You Lord,
   Praise You Lord.
   Wherever I am
   Your Spirit fills my life with song.

2. Whenever I can I will tell You Lord
   I love You.
   Wherever I am
   Your Spirit fills my heart with love.

3. Wherever I go I will serve You Lord,
   Serve You Lord
   Wherever I am
   Your Spirit fills my life with power.

4. Whatever I do I will need You Lord,
   Need You Lord.
   Wherever I am
   Your Spirit lives Your life through me.

284 Whether you're one

Words and Music
Graham Kendrick
arr. Phil Burt

Whether you're one or whether you're two Or three or four or five, Six or seven or eight or nine It's good to be a-live. It real-ly doesn't mat-ter how old you are, Jes-us loves you who-ev-er you are.

1. Whether you're one or whether you're two
   Or three or four or five,
   Six or seven or eight or nine
   It's good to be alive.
   It really doesn't matter how old you are,
   Jesus loves you whoever you are.

   La la la la la la la la la
   Jesus loves us all.
   La la la la la la la la la
   Jesus loves us all.

2. Whether you're big or whether you're small
   Or somewhere in between,
   First in the class or middle or last
   We're all the same to Him.
   It really doesn't matter how clever you are,
   Jesus loves you whoever you are.
       La la la la la la . . .

285 While shepherds watched

WINCHESTER OLD C.M.

First appeared in *Este's Psalter, 1592*

1. While shepherds watched their flocks by night,
   All seated on the ground,
   The angel of the Lord came down,
   And glory shone around:

2. 'Fear not!' said he (for mighty dread
   Had seized their troubled mind)
   'Glad tidings of great joy I bring
   To you and all mankind.

3. 'To you in David's town, this day
   Is born, of David's line,
   A Saviour, who is Christ the Lord;
   And this shall be the sign:

4. 'The heavenly babe you there shall find
   To human view displayed.
   All meanly wrapped in swaddling bands,
   And in a manger laid.'

5. Thus spake the angel; and forthwith
   Appeared a shining throng
   Of angels, praising God, who thus
   Addressed their joyful song:

6. 'All glory be to God on high,
   And to the earth be peace;
   Goodwill henceforth from heaven to men
   Begin and never cease.'

Nahum Tate, 1652-1715

286 Who took fish and bread?

ONLY JESUS

Words and music
Betty Lou Mills and
Russell J. Mills

Who took fish and bread, hun - gry peo - ple fed?

Who changed wa - ter in - to wine?

Who made well the sick, who made see the blind?

498

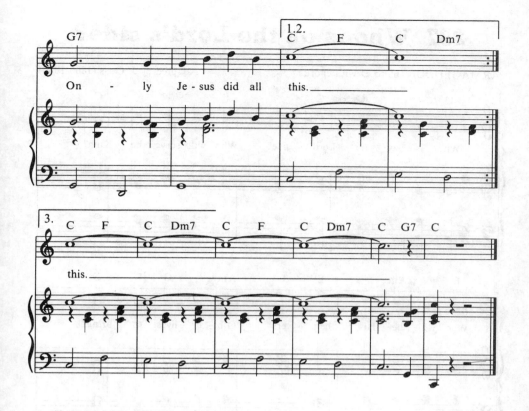

On - ly Je - sus did all this.

this.

1. Who took fish and bread, hungry people fed?
   Who changed water into wine?
   Who made well the sick, who made see the blind?
   Who touched earth with feet divine?
   Only Jesus, only Jesus, only He has done this:
   Who made live the dead? Truth and kindness spread?
   Only Jesus did all this.

2. Who walked dusty road? Cared for young and old?
   Who sat children on His knee?
   Who spoke words so wise? Filled men with suprise?
   Who gave all, but charged no fee?
   Only Jesus, only Jesus, only He has done this:
   Who in death and grief spoke peace to a thief?
   Only Jesus did all this.

3. Who soared through the air? Joined His Father there?
   He has you and me in view:
   He, who this has done, is God's only Son,
   And He's int'rested in you.
   Only Jesus, only Jesus, only He has done this:
   He can change a heart, give a fresh new start,
   Only He can do all this.

Betty Lou Mills & Russell J. Mills

287 Who is on the Lord's side?

ARMAGEDDON 65.65.D with chorus

Adapted by J. Goss (1800-1880)

Who is on the Lord's side? Who will serve the King?

Who will be His help - ers Oth - er lives to bring?

Who will leave the world's side? Who will face the foe?

Who is on the Lord's side? Who for Him will go?

By His call of mer-cy, Now our lives we bring,

We are on the Lord's side; Je-sus, He's our King.

1. Who is on the Lord's side?
   Who will serve the King?
   Who will be His helpers
   Other lives to bring?
   Who will leave the world's side?
   Who will face the foe?
   Who is on the Lord's side?
   Who for Him will go?

   By His call of mercy,
   Now our lives we bring,
   We are on the Lord's side;
   Jesus, He's our King.

2. Fierce may be the conflict,
   Strong may be the foe;
   But the King's own army
   None can overthrow.
   Round His standard ranging,
   Victory is secure;
   For His truth unchanging
   Makes the triumph sure.

   Joyfully enlisting,
   Now our lives we bring,
   We are on the Lord's side;
   Jesus, He's our King.

3. Chosen to be soldiers
   In an alien land,
   Chosen, called, and faithful,
   For our Captain's band,
   In the service royal
   Let us not grow cold;
   Let us be right loyal,
   Noble, true and bold.

   Master You will keep us,
   Serving You we sing:
   Always on the Lord's side,
   Jesus, always King.

Frances Ridley Havergal, 1836-1879
Altered © 1986 Horrobin / Leavers

501

288 Who put the colours in the rainbow?

Words and music
J.A.P. Booth
arr Douglas Coombes

Who put the col-ours in the rain - bow? Who put the salt in-to the sea? Who put the cold in-to the snow - flake? Who made you and me? Who put the hump upon the cam - el? Who put the neck on the gir - affe? Who put the tail upon the mon - key? Who made hy-e - nas

1. Who put the colours in the rainbow?
   Who put the salt into the sea?
   Who put the cold into the snowflake?
   Who made you and me?
   Who put the hump upon the camel?
   Who put the neck on the giraffe?
   Who put the tail upon the monkey?
   Who made hyenas laugh?
   Who made whales and snails and quails?
   Who made hogs and dogs and frogs?
   Who made bats and rats and cats?
   Who made ev'rything?

2. Who put the gold into the sunshine?
   Who put the sparkle in the stars?
   Who put the silver in the moonlight?
   Who made Earth and Mars?
   Who put the scent into the roses?
   Who taught the honey bee to dance?
   Who put the tree inside the acorn?
   It surely can't be chance!
   Who made seas and leaves and trees?
   Who made snow and winds that blow?
   Who made streams and rivers flow?
   God made all of these!

© *J.A.P. Booth*

289 Who's the king of the jungle

Words and music
Annie Bush
arr. Andy Silver

Who's the king of the jung-le? Who's the king of the sea? Who's the king of the u-ni-verse and who's the king of me? I'll tell you J-E-S-U-S is,

504

He's the king of me,
He's the king of the u-ni-verse, the jung-le and the sea.

Who's the king of the jungle?
Who's the king of the sea?
Who's the king of the universe and who's the king of me?
I'll tell you J-E-S-U-S is,
He's the king of me,
He's the king of the universe, the jungle and the sea.

290 Will your anchor hold

W. J. Kirkpatrick (1838–1921)

Will your an-chor hold in the storms of life, When the clouds un-fold their wings of strife? When the strong tides lift, and the ca - bles strain, Will your an - chor drift, or ___ firm re - main?

We have an-chor that keeps the soul Stead-fast and sure while the

bil - lows roll; Fastened to the rock which can - not move,

Groun - ded firm and deep in the Sav - iour's love!

1. Will your anchor hold in the storms of life,
   When the clouds unfold their wings of strife?
   When the strong tides lift, and the cables strain,
   Will your anchor drift, or firm remain?

   We have an anchor that keeps the soul
   Steadfast and sure while the billows roll;
   Fastened to the rock which cannot move,
   Grounded firm and deep in the Saviour's love!

2. Will your anchor hold in the straits of fear?
   When the breakers roar and the reef is near;
   While the waters rage, and the wild winds blow,
   Shall the angry waves then your life o'erflow?
   We have an anchor . . .

3. Will your anchor hold in the floods of death,
   When the waters cold chill your final breath?
   On the rising tide you can never fail,
   While your anchor holds within the veil.
   We have an anchor . . .

4. Will your eyes behold through the morning light
   The city of gold and the harbour bright?
   Will you anchor safe by the heavenly shore,
   When life's storms are past for evermore?
   We have an anchor . . .

Priscilla Jane Owens, 1829-1899

291 With Jesus in the boat

arr. Phil Burt

With Je-sus in the boat we can smile at the storm,

Smile at the storm, smile at the storm. With Je-sus in the boat we can

smile at the storm As we go sail-ing home.

Sail - ing, sail-ing home, Sail - ing,

With Jesus in the boat we can smile at the storm,
Smile at the storm, smile at the storm.
With Jesus in the boat we can smile at the storm
As we go sailing home.
Sailing, sailing home,
Sailing, sailing home,
With Jesus in the boat we can smile at the storm
As we go sailing home.

292 Wide, wide as the ocean

C. Austin Miles (1865–1946)

Wide, wide as the o-cean, high as the hea-ven a-bove;

Deep, deep as the deep-est sea is my Sa-viour's love.

I, though so un-wor-thy, still am a child of His care;

For His Word teaches me that His love reaches me ev-'ry-where.

Words and music © 1917, 1945 The Rodehaver Co./Word Music (UK) Ltd. Administered by
CopyCare Ltd, P O Box 77, Hailsham, East Sussex, BN27 3EF.

Wide, wide as the ocean, high as the heaven above;
Deep, deep as the deepest sea is my Saviour's love.
I, though so unworthy, still am a child of His care;
For His Word teaches me that His love reaches me everywhere.

293 Yes, God is good

WILLIAMS LM

From *Templi Carmina* (1829)

Capo 1

1. Yes, God is good—in earth and sky,
   From ocean depths and spreading wood,
   Ten thousand voices seem to cry:
   God made us all, and God is good.

2. The sun that keeps His trackless way,
   And downward pours His golden flood,
   Night's sparkling hosts, all seem to say
   In accents clear, that God is good.

3. The joyful birds prolong the strain,
   Their song with every spring renewed;
   The air we breathe, and falling rain,
   Each softly whispers: God is good.

4. I hear it in the rushing breeze;
   The hills that have for ages stood,
   The echoing sky and roaring seas,
   All swell the chorus: God is good.

5. Yes, God is good, all nature says,
   By God's own hand with speech endued;
   And man, in louder notes of praise,
   Should sing for joy that God is good.

6. For all Your gifts we bless You Lord,
   But chiefly for our heavenly food;
   Your pardoning grace, Your
                          quickening word,
   These prompt our song, that God is good.

John Hampden Gurney, 1802-1862

294 Yesterday, today, for ever

Capo 1

J. H. Burke (19th century)

Yes-ter-day, to-day, for ev-er, Je-sus is the same;
All may change, but Je-sus nev-er, Glo-ry to His Name!
Glo-ry to His Name! Glo-ry to His Name!
All may change, but Je-sus nev-er, Glo-ry to His Name!

Yesterday, today, for ever, Jesus is the same;
All may change, but Jesus never, Glory to His Name!
Glory to His Name! Glory to His Name!
All may change, but Jesus never, Glory to His Name!

A. B. Simpson, 1843–1919

295 Your ways are higher than mine

Words and music
Georgian Banov

Your ways are high-er than mine. Your ways are high-er than mine. Your ways are high-er than mine. Much high-er._____ Your ways are high-er than mine. Your ways are high-er than mine. Your ways are high-er than mine. Much high-

Hal - le - lu - jah, Hal - le - lu - jah, Hal - le - lu - jah, Hal - le - lu.

1. Your ways are higher than mine.
   Your ways are higher than mine.
   Your ways are higher than mine.
   Much higher.
   Your ways are higher than mine.
   Your ways are higher than mine.
   Your ways are higher than mine.
   Much higher.
   Higher, higher, much, much, higher,
   Higher, higher, much higher.
   Higher, higher, much, much, higher,
   Higher, higher, much higher.

2. Your thoughts are wiser than mine.
   Your thoughts are wiser than mine.
   Your thoughts are wiser than mine.
   Much wiser.
   Your thoughts are wiser than mine.
   Your thoughts are wiser than mine.
   Your thoughts are wiser than mine.
   Much wiser.
   Wiser, wiser, much, much, wiser,
   Wiser, wiser, much wiser.
   Wiser, wiser, much, much, wiser,
   Wiser, wiser, much wiser.

3. Your strength is greater than mine.
   Your strength is greater than mine.
   Your strength is greater than mine.
   Much greater.
   Your strength is greater than mine.
   Your strength is greater than mine.
   Your strength is greater than mine.
   Much greater.
   Greater, greater, much, much, greater,
   Greater, greater, much greater.
   Greater, greater, much, much, greater,
   Greater, greater, much greater.

   Hallelujah, Hallelujah,
   Hallelujah, Hallelu.
   Hallelujah, Hallelujah,
   Hallelujah, Hallelu.

296 You are the King of glory

Words and music
M. Ford

Capo 3

With Majesty

You are the King of Glo-ry, You are the Prince of Peace, You are the Lord of heav'n and earth, You're the Son of righteous - ness. An-gels bow down be - fore You, Wor - ship and a - dore, for

516

You have the words of e-ter-nal life,___ You are Je-sus Christ the
Lord. ____ Ho - san-na to the Son of Da - vid! ____ Ho -
san-na to the King of ___ kings! Glo-ry in the high-est
hea - ven, For Je-sus the Mess-i - ah reigns.

You are the King of Glory,
You are the Prince of Peace,
You are the Lord of heav'n and earth,
You're the Son of righteousness.
Angels bow down before You,
Worship and adore, for

You have the words of eternal life,
You are Jesus Christ the Lord.
Hosanna to the Son of David!
Hosanna to the King of kings!
Glory in the highest heaven,
For Jesus the Messiah reigns.

517

297 You can't stop rain from falling down

J. Larson

You can't stop rain from fall-ing down, Pre-vent the sun from shi - ning, You can't stop spring from com-ing in, Or win-ter from re - sign-ing, Or still the waves or stay the winds, Or

keep the day from dawn - ing; You can't stop God from

lov - ing you, His love is new each morn - ing.

1. You can't stop rain from falling down,
   Prevent the sun from shining,
   You can't stop spring from coming in,
   Or winter from resigning,
   Or still the waves or stay the winds,
   Or keep the day from dawning;
   You can't stop God from loving you,
   His love is new each morning.

2. You can't stop ice from being cold,
   You can't stop fire from burning,
   Or hold the tide that's going out,
   Delay its sure returning,
   Or halt the progress of the years,
   The flight of fame and fashion;
   You can't stop God from loving you,
   His nature is compassion.

3. You can't stop God from loving you,
   Though you may disobey Him,
   You can't stop God from loving you,
   However you betray Him;
   From love like this no pow'r on earth
   The human heart can sever,
   You can't stop God from loving you,
   Not God, not now, nor ever.

J. Gowans

519

298 Your hand, O God

THORNBURY 76.76.D

Basil Harwood (1859-1949)

Capo 2

Your hand, O God has gui - ded Your
flock, from age to age; Your faith-ful-ness is
writ - ten On his-tory's o - pen page. Our
fa - thers knew Your good - ness, And we their deeds re -

1. Your hand, O God has guided
   Your flock, from age to age;
   Your faithfulness is written
   On history's open page.
   Our fathers knew Your goodness,
   And we their deeds record;
   And both to this bear witness:
   One church, one faith, One Lord.

2. Your heralds brought the gospel
   To greatest as to least;
   They summoned men to hasten
   And share the great king's feast.
   And this was all their teaching
   In every deed and word;
   To all alike proclaiming:
   One church, one faith, One Lord.

3. Through many days of darkness,
   Through many scenes of strife,
   The faithful few fought bravely
   To guard the nation's life.
   Their gospel of redemption—
   Sin pardoned, man restored;
   Was all in this enfolded:
   One church, one faith, One Lord.

4. Your mercy will not fail us
   Nor leave Your work undone;
   With Your right hand to help us,
   The victory shall be won.
   And then by earth and heaven
   Your name shall be adored;
   And this shall be their anthem:
   One church, one faith, One Lord.

E.H. Plumptre, 1821-1891

521

299 Yours be the glory!

MACCABAEUS 10.11.11.11 with chorus

Capo 4

G.F. Handel (1685-1759)

Yours be the glo-ry! ri-sen, con-quering Son;

End-less is the vict-ory o-ver death You won;

An-gels robed in splen-dour rolled the stone a-way,

Kept the fold-ed grave clothes where Your bo-dy lay:

1. Yours be the glory! risen, conquering Son;
   Endless is the victory over death You won;
   Angels robed in splendour rolled the stone away,
   Kept the folded grave clothes where Your body lay:

   Yours be the glory! risen, conquering Son:
   Endless is the victory over death You won.

2. See! Jesus meets us, risen from the tomb,
   Lovingly he greets us, scatters fear and gloom;
   Let the church with gladness hymns of triumph sing!
   For her Lord is living, death has lost its sting
   Yours be the glory . . .

3. No more we doubt you, glorious prince of life:
   What is life without you? aid us in our strife;
   Make us more than conquerors, through your deathless love,
   Bring us safe through Jordan to your home above:
   Yours be the glory . . .

after E.L. Budry, 1854-1932
R.B. Hoyle, 1875-1939
© *World Student Christian Federation,*
in this version *Jubilate Hymns*

300 Zaccheus was a very little man

Luke 19.4

Anon. arr. J.W.

Zac-che-us was a ve-ry lit-tle man, And a ve-ry lit-tle man was he. He climbed up in-to a sy-ca-more tree, For the Sa-viour he wan-ted to see. And when the Sa-viour passed that way, He looked in-to the tree and

524

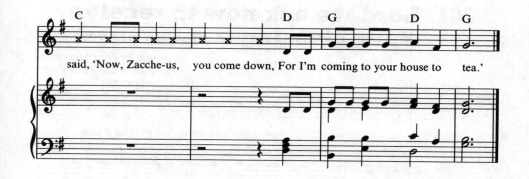

said, 'Now, Zacche-us, you come down, For I'm coming to your house to tea.'

Zaccheus was a very little man,
And a very little man was he.
He climbed up into a sycamore tree,
For the Saviour he wanted to see.
And when the Saviour passed that way,
He looked into the tree and said,
'Now, Zaccheus, you come down,
For I'm coming to your house to tea.'

Copyright control

301 Lord we ask now to receive Your blessing (A closing prayer)

Music by Peter Horrobin,
Phil Burt and Greg Leavers

Lord we ask now to re-ceive Your bles-sing,

Lord we ask now to re-ceive Your love.

Come, we pray; Come, we pray And

lead us hour by hour.___

Bless, we ask, our friends and close re - la - tions

Let them feel Your touch of lov - ing power.

1. Lord we ask now to receive Your blessing,
   Lord we ask now to receive Your love.
   Come, we pray; Come, we pray
   And lead us hour by hour.
   Bless, we ask, our friends and close relations
   Let them feel Your touch of loving power.

2. Lord we trust You to give us Your blessing,
   Lord we trust You to give us Your love
   As we give; As we give
   Our lives afresh to You.
   Take, we ask, all that we have and are, Lord,
   Let them now be used in service true.

3. Lord we give to others now Your blessing,
   Lord we give to others now Your love.
   As we share; As we share
   With them the life You've giv'n.
   Yes we will in harmony with You, Lord,
   Let them see in us a touch of heav'n.

Notes for Guitarists

An important part of the concept for this book is the addition of guitar chords to the music for all the hymns and songs. For in a growing number of church and school situations the guitar is an important instrument for leading singing and worship.

We appreciate that the experience and ability of guitarists varies considerably and we have, therefore, attempted to make the arrangements as simple as possible without destroying the richness of the music. We suggest that if your chord knowledge is currently very limited that it would be well worthwhile learning a few more chords (e.g. F#m, C#m, Bm, Gm, B♭ and diminished chords), for you would then be able to play nearly all the hymns and songs we have included.

To enable relatively simple chords to be regularly used we have often included two sets of chords, so that with the use of a capo, as directed at the top of the music, the guitarist can follow the set of easier bracketed chords e.g. E♭ (D).

We want guitarists to enjoy their playing, but we also want to encourage those with limited ability to learn new chords and techniques. Here are a few practical tips:

1. Practice strumming so that you learn what types of rhythm suit particular sorts of hymn. If you have a steel strung guitar, get used to using a plectrum.
2. Be confident when you lead. Practice does make an enormous difference! You will find that people will sing confidently if you play confidently.
3. Learn the chords well so that you don't have to stop half way through a song to look one up in the chord chart.
4. Make sure your guitar is in tune, (i) with itself, and (ii) with any other instrument you're playing along with.
5. Make sure you and any other instrument player know what key you are going to play a particular song in.
6. Lastly, but most importantly, pray about your music. Don't just treat it as a hobby but see it as a privilege to lead others in worship and singing.

Greg Leavers

Using the Chord Chart

This chart contains all the chords you will need to play all the hymns and songs in this book. Even if a chord looks more difficult than those you are used to playing, DO TRY. Always seek to improve your knowledge and playing ability. It may seem to you that you have a very large number of chords to learn, but don't panic! For example, look at Fm, F#m, Gm, and G#m, and you will see that they all have the same finger formation, but are on different frets for each chord. So, if you learn the ONE finger formation, you can immediately play *four new chords!*

If you want to play chords in a different key to the one set (because, for example, of a limited chord knowledge) you can very simply use this chart to discover the chords you need. Here's how you do it:

1. Locate the key chord that is set in the original. Find it on the chart in the SECOND COLUMN for the *major* keys and the THIRD COLUMN for *minor* keys.
2. Locate on the chart the new key that you wish to play the music in (also in the second column for *major* keys and the third column for *minor* keys).
3. Work out the rest of the chords that need to be changed by noting their position around the original key chord and finding the chord that is *in exactly the same position* around the new key chord.

Example:

When changing from key chord F to key chord E, find F and E in the second column of the chart. On the left of F you will find C7. The equivalent chord in key E is therefore the one on the left of E, B7. Similarly Dm would become C#m, and B♭ would become A.

Chord Chart

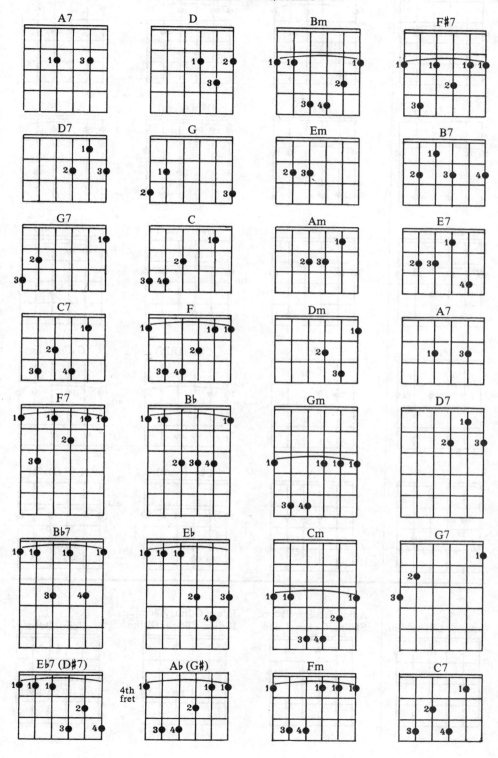

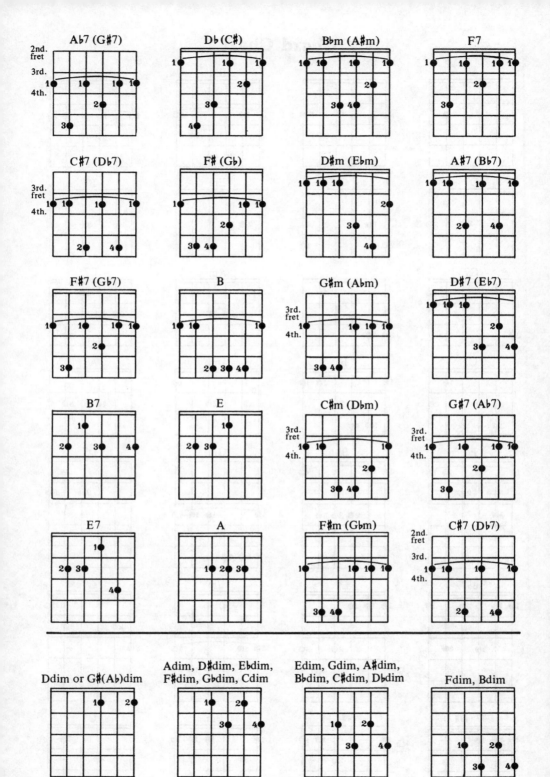

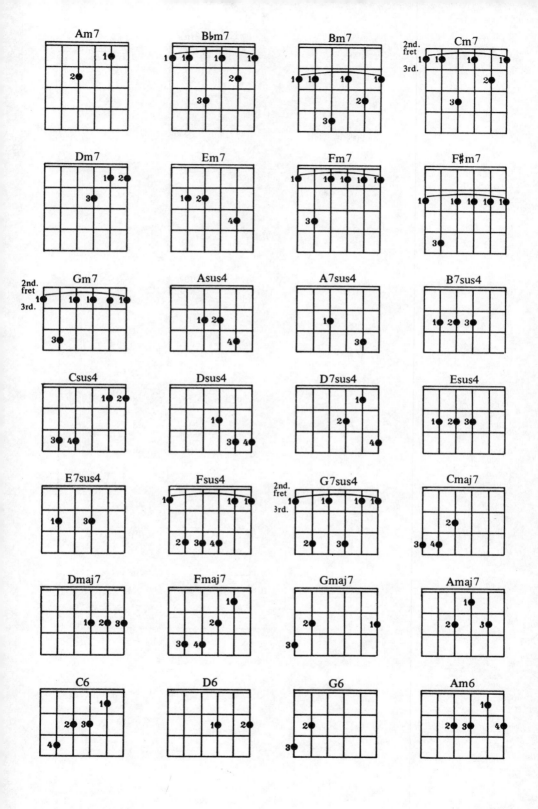

Subject Index

Index of first Lines

Titles which differ from first lines are shown in italics

Copyright Addresses

Alexander (Charles M)'s Copyright Trust c/o S. W. Grant, 12 Lawrie Park Crescent, Sydenham, London SE26 6HD

Allen, C. J. and G. F., Executors of G. F. Allen, c/o Mrs G. R. Windows, Lloyds Private Banking, P O Box 126, Bank House, Wine Street, Bristol BS99 7LG

Arlott, J., Executors of J. Arlott, c/o Mrs B. P. Arlott, 5 Queen Elizabeth II Street, Alderney, CI

Barham-Gould, A. C., c/o D. R. Gould, 34 Pollard Drive, Horsham, West Sussex RH13 5HH

Barrows, Cliff, Melody Lane, Rt 9 No Parker Road, Greenville, South Carolina 29609 USA

A & C Black (Publishers) Ltd, Howard Road, Eaton Socon, Huntingdon, Cambs PE19 3EZ

Boosey & Hawkes Music Publishers Ltd, 295 Regent's Street, London W1R 8JH

J. A. P. Booth, 187 Walmsworth Road, Doncaster, S. Yorks DN4 OTW

Bosworth & Co Ltd, 14/18 Heddon Street, London W1R 8DP

Brattle, Gordon, c/o N. A. M. Cooke, P O Box 201, West Malling, Kent ME19 5RS

Breitkopf und Härtel, Buch und Musikverlag, Walkmuhlstrasse 52, D-6200, Weisbaden, Germany

Burt, Phil, 5 Gardner Road, Warton, Carnforth, Lancs LA5 9NY

Bush, Annie c/o Mrs A Spears, 5 Henglers Close, Everton, Liverpool L6 1NJ

Cansdale, J. H., 12 Belfield Close, Weymouth, Dorset DT4 9RG

Chappell Music Ltd, 129 Park Street, London W1Y 3FA

Christian Music Ministries, 325 Bromfield Road, Hodge Hill, Birmingham B36 8ET

Cliff College, Calver, Sheffield S30 1XD

CopyCare Ltd, P O Box 77, Hailsham, East Sussex BN27 3EF

Dudley-Smith, Timothy, 9 Ashlands, Ford, Salisbury, Wilts SP4 6DY

William Elkin Music Services Ltd, Station Road Industrial Estate, Salhouse, Norwich, Norfolk NR13 6NY

EMI Music Publishing Ltd, 127 Charing Cross Road, London WC2H OLD

Franciscan Communications, 1229 South Santee Street, Los Angeles, California 90015, USA

Fudge, Roland, High Grain, Austwick, Lancaster LA2 8AN

Gill, D. M., Kerry Hill, Hawling, Andoversford, Glos GL54 5SZ

Hall, Archie, Lochinver, 69 King George V Avenue, Kings Lynn, Norfolk PE30 2QE

Harper, Jeanne, Stanfords, 27 Muster Green, Haywards Heath, West Sussex RH16 8JB

HarperCollins*Religious*, c/o CopyCare Ltd, P O Box 77, Hailsham, East Sussex BN27 3EF

David Higham Associates, 5–8 Lower John Street, Golden Square, London W1R 4HA

High-Fye Music, Campbell Connelly Co Ltd, 8–9 Frith Street, London W1R 4HA

Hope Publishing Company, 380 South Main Place, Carol Stream, Illinois 60188, USA

Horrobin, P. J., Ellel Grange, Ellel, Carnforth, Lancs LA2 OHN

Integrity Music Europe Ltd, Berkeley House, 26 Gildredge Road, Eastbourne, East Sussex BN21 3UX

Jones, Ron, 2 Dean Avenue, Wallasey Village, Cheshire

Jubilate Hymns, c/o Mrs Bunty Grundy, 61 Chessel Avenue, Southampton SO19 4DY

Kerr, B. K. M., Wayside Cottage, East Dean, Eastbourne, East Sussex BN20 OBP

Kingsway's Thankyou Music, P O Box 75, Eastbourne, East Sussex BN23 6NW

Leavers, Greg, 1 Haws Hill, Carnforth, Lancs LA5 9DD

Leosong Copyright Service Ltd, 123 Westmead Road, Sutton, Surrey SM1 4JH

Lindsay Music, 23 Hitchin Street, Biggleswade, Beds SG18 8AX

McCrimmon Publishing Company, 10–12 High Street, Great Wakering, Essex SS3 OEQ

Meredith, Rev Roland, 1 Deanery Court, Broad Street, Bampton, Oxon OX18 2LY

Methodist Publishing House, 20 Ivatt Way, Peterborough, Cambs PE3 7PG

National Christian Education Council, 1020 Bristol Road, Selly Oak, Birmingham B29 6LB

Oxford University Press, 3 Park Road, London NW1 6XN

Public Trustee Office, Stewart House, Kingsway, London WC2B 6JX

Rusbridge, R., 9 Springfield House, Cotham, Bristol BS6 6DQ

Salvationist Publishing and Supplies Ltd, 117–121 Judd Street, London WC1H 9NN

Scott, Lestria, 5 Church Street, Pershore, Worcs WR10 1D7

Scripture Gift Mission, Radstock House, 3 Ecclestone Street, London SW1W 9LZ

Scripture in Song, c/o Integrity Music Europe Ltd, Berkeley House, 26 Gildredge Road, Eastbourne, East Sussex BN21 3UX

Scripture Union, 207–9 Queensway, Bletchley, Bucks MK2 2EB

Sheldon, Robin, Music in Worship, 151 Bath Road, Hounslow, Middlesex TW3 3BO

Silver, Andy, Bell House Farm, Dalton, Burton-in-Kendal, Lancs LA6 1NN

Simmonds, C, School House, 81 Clapham Road, Bedford MK41 7RB

Simpson, Annie and Neil, 9 Mungosnelly

New from Marshall Pickering Music . . .

If you've enjoyed using *Junior Praise*, why not try *Junior Praise 2*, an exciting new supplement with 200 more items to add to the 300 in Book 1?

A new combined words edition is also available, containing the words for all 500 items.

Music edition (hardback) ISBN 0 551 02480 1
Combined words edition (paperback) ISBN 0 551 02639 1
Combined words edition (hardback) ISBN 0 551 02638 3